REACHING NEW HEIGHTS

Robert McAvoy and Lauren Early

Reaching New Heights

ISBN: 978-0-9933110-1-7

Contents

Disclaimer

The information in this book is meant to supplement, not replace Irish dance training. Like any sport involving speed, equipment, balance and environmental factors, strength and conditioning training poses some inherent risk. The authors advise readers to take full responsibility for their safety and know their limits. Before practising the skills described in this book, be sure that your equipment is well maintained, and do not take risks beyond your level of experience, training ability and comfort level. The training methods described within this book are that of the authors' personal thoughts, experiences and past training outcomes. They are not intended to be a definitive set of instructions for this sport. You may discover that there are other methods and materials that accomplish the same end result.

This book is designed to provide condensed information at a basic entry level for strength and conditioning for Irish dancing. It is not intended to reprint, teach or compile all the information that is otherwise available, but instead complement, amplify and supplement other texts to aid in advancing your current training regime. As this book is providing information to people of different ages and genders across the world, you are urged to read all available material, learn as much as possible and tailor the information to your own needs.

The training and nutrition programmes are provided to the

reader as examples and are not to be followed for your own use. Please consult your doctor or dietician before starting any training or nutritional programmes.

Every effort has been made to make this book as complete and as accurate as possible. However there may be mistakes, both typographical and in content, and therefore this text should be used only as a general guide and not as the ultimate source of information. The purpose of this book is to educate. The authors shall accept no responsibility or liability to any person or entity with respect to any loss, damage or injury caused, or alleged to have been caused, directly or indirectly by the information contained in this book.

About the authors

To date Lauren Early is one of the highest-achieving dancers of all time. Lauren is a six times back-to-back World Irish Dance champion, a five times All Ireland champion, twelve times Ulster champion, six times All Scotland champion, six times Great Britain champion, American national champion and a British national champion.

After Lauren stopped competitive and show dancing she quickly turned her attention to what she could give back to the sport. Lauren recognised the lack of support and resources available to our sport and set out to change the world of Irish dancing forever. She has spent the last two years of her life conducting workshops and seminars teaching the importance of having a professional strength and conditioning structure set up for all Irish dancers.

Lauren soon realised it was impossible to educate everyone based on workshops and seminars alone and therefore turned her attention to writing the first strength and conditioning book for competitive Irish dancers. She has dedicated a whole year of her life to putting together this book you are holding so that everyone in the sport can receive the help and support they deserve, regardless of their location or association.

In 2016 Lauren will be applying to sit the TCRG (Teagascóir Choimisiúin le Rinci Gaelacha) exam and, once qualified as a teacher of Irish dance, she will open up the very first Irish Dance, Strength and Performance Centres for her own dancing schools. Location – worldwide.

With Lauren's visions and dedication it is clear that strength and conditioning will play a very big part in competitive Irish dance from this moment on.

Robert McAvoy is a former UK 400 m hurdles international athlete. Upon leaving school Robert competed for both the UK and Ireland as one of the fastest 400 m hurdlers in the country.

After injury caused an end to competition, Robert went on to establish his own coaching set up within the athletics community in the UK. His great sporting talents quickly turned to effective coaching talents as results started to come and people started to take notice of the work Robert was doing locally.

In 2008 Robert became firstly a personal trainer and later a national strength and conditioning coach as he started branching out into other sports and gaining worldwide recognition. It wasn't long before Robert's coaching talents became known to TV personalities, film crews, actors and other top profile clients and to date has acquired multiple BAFTA and Golden Globe award winning clientele.

At the time of writing this book Robert is recognised as one of the top strength coaches and personal trainers in the UK. In athletic performance Robert has developed world class athletes in eleven different sports. These athletes are spread around the world, from sporting set ups in Australia, USA, Canada and Europe, as well as locally based in the UK and Ireland.

As well as his current responsibilities Robert dedicates time to ongoing Irish dance workshops and seminars, visiting schools with Lauren Early to conduct world class education across the globe.

Important message from Lauren

My journey from being a young, unknown girl in Belfast to becoming a six times World Irish Dance champion has been an incredible experience and it has inspired me to write this book you are holding. Within these pages I have given you all the tools necessary for any dancer to reach the top, but before you get started I feel it's important to highlight one thing.

Success is not something that can be given to you, it must be earned. It takes hard work, dedication, commitment, desire, and hunger to succeed more than anything in the world. Many will not reach the top; however, the real victory comes not only from becoming the best dancer you can be, but the person you become as a result of this journey, that's what truly makes each of us a champion!

The title of this book is *Reaching New Heights*. It is my aim to ensure that each and every one of you not only develops and becomes a better dancer, teacher, parent or school, but more importantly develops as a person. Throughout this book I want you to acknowledge your strengths and develop your weaknesses, take control of your self-confidence, avoid negativity, have belief in yourself and passion for what you truly believe in. Always remember the reason why you started Irish dancing – find your passion in life. Set goals and never stop until you achieve them.

I promise each of you that by the end of your journey you will all have **Reached New Heights.**

Lauren Early

Introduction – My journey so far

I started Irish dancing when I was five years old. At that age I did not know anything about Irish dancing and in fact had never even seen it performed before. My mum, Kate, sent me and my two sisters – Katrina, who was eight, and Jennifer, who was ten – to our very first Irish dance class. Apparently we were driving her crazy in the house one day – with my little brother Nathan, who was one, screaming in the background – and she said she had to send us out for an hour. Little did we know I was about to take my very first step on a journey that would turn me into a world champion.

I remember my first ever dance class. My mum had got me and my two sisters brand new dancing pumps. I remember opening the box like it was Christmas, the smell of the leather escaping from our brand new vanity cases, each of us telling the others that our shoes were best when in fact they were all exactly the same.

We arrived at the hall whispering between ourselves, all so very excited for our first ever Irish dance class. My sisters pushed me in first, as apparently I was the cheeky show off out of the three of us (*well, that's what they said!*).

I remember walking into a massive, cold, spacious room (*which I thought it was at that time*). I suddenly felt overwhelmed by it all, as I'm sure any five-year-old would – the loud Irish dancing music, the sound of hard shoes tapping on the floor and the huge number of kids in class. Being overwhelmed lasted about five minutes. I remember taking a deep breath and immediately wanting to get out there, I was super-excited to start learning fast and to meet new friends. Once I'd started I didn't care who was watching or if I was doing it right or wrong, I just wanted to dance and perform for people. I loved the excitement of stepping out in front of everyone in class to show off my new dance moves and so as a kid this was my motivation in class – I worked hard to have the chance to show others what I could do!

I loved having my sisters with me, too, as they would always help me with new steps and they encouraged me to learn more and work hard at it. Even though we were all still very young we all knew what we wanted out of dancing, and that was to perform, win medals and make our parents proud of us. I worked so hard at it because I had the love of Irish dance. I guess once you have the love for it you're attached to it somehow for life. My dancing teachers moved me on quickly as I was picking the dances up a lot better than the other beginners.

Once my teachers started entering me for competitions I started winning first place again and again. Sometimes I would place in top five, top three, or achieve first place, depending on the day and how I performed. Being a young kid, nerves didn't come into the equation; I just got up on stage, beaming ear to ear, my head held high, watching and smiling at my parents the whole time as I showed off what I had learned in class. I never thought about results, I just wanted a shiny medal to take home to show my grandparents and friends.

I will never forget the first time I walked into a feis; the atmosphere was intense, the hall was packed with dancers, friends and families. I always had my family and grandparents there supporting me so that always boosted my confidence and got me excited to get up on stage.

I will never forget the smell of hairspray and spray tan which permeated all through the venue. It was my first time experiencing that competition effect and those smells will stay with me for life. All my family were more than proud of me, and my mum and dad knew that their daughter was in it for the long run. Every dancer's parents worked very hard at their jobs to provide money to buy Irish dancing dresses, wigs, tan, sock glue, socks, pumps, heavies etc., and mine also had to work hard.

We sit and laugh today about how they coped with three young girls dancing and the drama it caused and the cost that came with it. I don't know how my parents did it! The sacrifices and trade-offs that parents have to make, even at this early beginner stage, is often unjustifiable and credit must go to both my parents *(and all the parents reading this)* who made it possible.

My first major championship was the Ulster Championships. I

was only ten years old, going down to Newry (N. Ireland) to do my first ever major. Of course as always I had my family with me for support. I was super-thrilled as I had got my first handmade solo dress – made by Mrs Graham – and I wanted to wear it in the car for the journey down.

The morning of my competition all sorts of feelings were running through my head and my stomach. I was excited but anxious, I was nervous but calm, I noticed at this age I really understood more about what I was doing and what competition was really all about. Sometimes not knowing makes you fearless whereas knowing creates doubt – I told myself I must either choose to have a fear of the stage or a love of the stage. I chose to love the stage and not to be afraid of the big audience. I understood the challenge that I was faced with and I accepted it. I told myself I only get one shot at every dance and that there was no space in my mind for doubt or fear. I knew when I stepped off the stage I would run to my mum and at that point I couldn't fix any mistakes or hiccups, or change the past – I had to perform at my best right now.

We had to wait a few hours for the recalls to be announced, and those few hours felt like a lifetime. I remember torturing my poor mummy, saying, 'Are they out yet? Are they out yet?', repeating the same sentence over and over again. Looking back, I really don't know how she managed.

Finally a voice came on the microphone from behind the stage announcing the recall numbers for the last dance. Squeezing my mum's hand I started to pray for my number to come out. I could feel the excitement in my stomach; knowing I had to get picked to be watched again was brand new to me and I knew I needed to perform this last dance amazingly to get a good result.

"Yes!!!" Mum and I squeezed each other's hands as my number came out. Everyone's eyes lit up, they were ecstatic for me. We kept our excitement inside as other numbers were still getting called. My first Ulster championships and I got my first recall – the day couldn't have got any better. I remember feeling like I was on top of the world. It's a very precious moment and an excellent achievement to get a recall at a major, and any dancer reading this will share the same feelings with me. *(For those who haven't experienced this yet, I will do my very best throughout this book to get you there!)*

Sitting on my mum's knee and squeezing the blood out of her hand, my first mark came out: 'One hundred.' I let out a tiny scream of excitement, my mum telling me, 'Ssh, it's not over yet!' At this stage my mum and I were turning purple, we were squeezing each other so hard. Being young, I didn't realise that the next mark could be a ten or a five; my mum and sisters made me realise you can't get too excited until your full marks are out, and I learned that a lot as I got older.

Next mark: 'One hundred.' Last mark: 'One hundred.' Total:

'Three hundred.' I immediately started crying my eyes out! My family, friends and dance teachers cheered and clapped, and other people I didn't know joined in also. I felt like I had just won the World Championships. I couldn't believe that I was the chosen winner, that they thought I was that good to get straight hundreds across the board. I sopped on my mum's shoulder – what an amazing memory, I'll never ever forget. What an achievement.

From that date I went on to win the Ulster Championships for another twelve years back-to-back and each win was just as special as the last. However, there is always something so special about your first victory; still to this day I can't believe it, those memories will stay with me forever.

Dancing my first ever All Ireland Championships I placed fifth. I was still young and couldn't believe I'd achieved such an amazing place for my very first time. Again, the older and more experienced I became I realised nerves started to kick in more as I danced at majors, but thank God I still had the excitement to compete.

After my first year I placed fourth, then third, then second. Finally, after a lot of years of hard work, tears, tantrums, patience and belief, I got to the top and won my first All Ireland title at the age of thirteen.

Wow, what an unreal experience! It was in my home town,

Belfast (N. Ireland), and so all my family were there – aunts, uncles, cousins grandparents – I couldn't have imagined a more perfect, nerve-racking, adrenaline-rush of a day.

At this age I clearly understood who my top competitors were, what I needed to do to win and how to control my nerves to not mess up on stage. It is at this age and this stage I believe it can go either way for a dancer. You can let the expectation get the better of you or you can take control and develop a way to deal with it.

I still see myself as a silent champion. Of course I didn't want anyone knowing my secrets, I never would boast about my winnings and I never walked around like I was someone important. Ultimately, though, I never ever took winning for granted. I truly believe that once you start taking winning for granted you become a person that no one wants to aspire to. I knew I had hard work to do, I knew there were great dancers below me clicking at my heels and so I had to focus my energy on staying one step ahead.

I went on to win another four All Ireland titles after my first win. Writing this now I still can't believe and accept these achievements, in a way time went so fast that I couldn't take it all in. I guess this is why your first victory will always be the most special as you have time to appreciate what has just happened without the expectation.

I remember dancing my first World Championships like it was yesterday. It was held in Glasgow at the NEC, which is a huge arena. The *Pop Idol* concert was also on that weekend in the same complex. I remember that clearly, with the flashing lights outside my bedroom window at our hotel. It was attached to the NEC so it was handy for walking to the venue.

I remember seeing others taping up their toes, and I too then started to tape up my own toes with gel plasters, about ten times, even though I hadn't one blister on them. I thought that the extra cushioning would be good. I think I smothered my feet, to be honest, and I never made that mistake again.

On stage there were seven judges looking at me. I knew I was dancing against the top people in the world and I placed third that day. How unreal, I thought life couldn't get any better!

The feedback I got was that my fringe was too long and the judges couldn't see my face. At the time I didn't understand this feedback from my teacher to my mum, but it goes to show stage presence is so important and that was my first experience of having to deal with it. I went away having listened to the feedback and changed what was required.

After my first World Championships in 2002, I placed fourth in 2003, second in 2004 and second in 2005. In 2006 my life was about to change. I finally understood what was required to become a champion. I put together training programmes, nutrition programmes, wrote a weekly training diary and made lifestyle changes to live my first year as a proper athlete should. I tracked everything in my log book: how fast I was, how high I could jump, how much water I had drunk, how much food I had eaten and how much sleep I had had. I just didn't stop writing. This training journal was my Bible and each month I looked back on my performance for the previous weeks and made sure I done better.

It paid off – from 2006-2011 I won all six world titles back-to-back! That's when I knew how important it was to have an athletic set up in place and ultimately that's what has inspired me to write this book for you. The difference between competing in dancing as a hobby and treating myself like an athlete was the biggest change in my career. Taking that first step to acknowledge that you are an athlete and that you must adopt an athlete's lifestyle is the start of you reaching your potential.

From the age of seventeen up I went and toured with the show *Lord of the Dance* when I wasn't training for a competition. I went to Taiwan, Germany, Switzerland, France, Abu Dhabi and many other great countries. It was a brilliant experience, being so young and enjoying show dancing, which is completely different from competitive dancing. I enjoyed having no pressure and actually saw dancing from a completely different perspective. I also had to adapt my training as competitive Irish dance is completely different in length than show dancing, and therefore I had to adopt a different approach to balance the two.

I stopped dancing with *Lord of the Dance* the same year I finished competing at my last World Championships. I knew my love for performing in front of people was slowly going. I no longer had that competitive edge in me. Without realising it, I had started taking the focus off my own training and was instead becoming a mentor for the younger dancers coming through. I began to help others with their training schedules and provide advice to those who wanted it. I found a new sense of achievement in helping others achieve results, even more so than the enjoyment I was getting from my own results.

In my last World Championship I placed third. For the two months leading up to it I worked super hard, as always, and as a professional I performed as well as I could. I wouldn't take back how I danced that day as I was immensely proud of myself, as were my teachers and family. I watched the other competitors and they were lovely. I thought I would have placed higher, but we can't always get what we want. I'd just won six world titles back-to-back and not many dancers can say that. Everything happens for a reason, I believe this reason was a sign that it was my time to move on and give back to the sport that I have achieved everything in, and that's exactly what I did ...

My motivation for writing this book is to change the world of competitive Irish dance forever by introducing the very first strength and conditioning handbook specifically for competitive Irish dance. I'm giving back everything that I have learnt. I want to be your mentor and I will not stop working until I bring the level of support and resources for our sport up to a similar standard of other sports around the world. I hope by reading this that I'll inspire you to fight for what you want and believe in. I hope to teach you more about you as a person and help you learn how to achieve those goals you desire.

Just like when I stepped into my first dance hall at the age of five, not realising that I was taking my first step towards becoming a champion, I want you all to realise that by holding this book you, too, have just taken the first step towards becoming your own champion.

Close your eyes, take a deep breath and visualise what you want to get out of this book. Now keep that thought in your head the whole way through.

Are you ready to walk this journey with me???

Let's go!

PART 1

YOUR JOURNEY STARTS HERE

Overview

My story, which I share throughout this book, is proof that any dancer out there can achieve their goals and reach the very top given they have the desire, hunger and a work ethic like no one else.

Whether your goal is to have no fear of the stage, to get a recall, to place top twenty at Worlds or to get that number one spot – if you want to be successful, then adopting the principles within *Reaching New Heights* will get you there.

Any dreamer, anyone with the passion and drive to transcend the ordinary, will find this book helpful.

I put together my beliefs and honest facts in this book to make you the best you can be and to take you to the very peak of your performance. I am going to seek out and develop that strong, confident person within you. By the end of this book you will have a mindset so powerful you'll know you can achieve anything you want to.

I am about to share everything I have learnt and experienced throughout my career in competitive Irish dance. I discuss the mindset required to become number one, my secret techniques, my failures, the training and the dedication required to be the best you can be.

It is always going to impossible to meet the needs of every reader of every age and level of ability reading this book. I understand that some chapters might be more confusing than others, but don't panic – you will start to develop a clear picture and as you go on to read further chapters, everything will start to click together.

After every chapter there is a summary box pointing out the key points covered to make sure that you have picked up everything correctly and to remind you of the key take home points. I strongly recommend you write these down as you go.

At the back of the book there is also a 'Useful information' section covering the main areas of the whole book. It includes key areas such as training programmes, nutrition plans, questionnaires and reference tables, which means that all the training information given throughout the book is collected together for ease of reference when you are referring back for guidance.

Before we get there I hope to make you guys laugh out loud along the way, I want you to cry, I want to bring home the importance of you having your own targets and goals, not just for dancing, but also for life. I want you to circle, highlight, underline and take notes throughout to help you take it all in.

Finally, I want you to think for a second. Ask yourself, 'Do I want to be more successful? Do I want to improve my performance? Do I want to go as far as I can?' If your answer is no, then please pass this book on to someone who wants to be the best they can be. If your answer is yes, this book is definitely for you. Let's get started by making an impact together.

This book isn't about me, *Reaching New Heights* is about you!

We've got to find your perfect gear to get started in, but first you must start your engine. You must already have the fuel in the tank to want this before I steer you in the right direction to drive things forward. Are you ready to move that gear stick with me?

Are you frightened? Well, I'm not, I can't wait to get started with you.

You've made the decision that you are going to be the best you can be.

Let's make YOU a huge success.

Ready? Let's go!

Chapter 1
Finding yourself

Being you is important. Every single one of us has been made differently, everyone brings a unique quality in who they are, and everyone is special. Do not hide your uniqueness, do not hide you. Let's begin by finding the real you!

You are the average of the five people you spend the most time with

Your success depends on the people you surround yourself with. The hard-working, determined people, the people who you look at and say to yourself, 'I want to be just like them'. You are a combination of the five people you spend your utmost time around. We all try and gel with others so that we can all get along and feel like we are fitting in. Just be aware that it is the right people you want to gel with and keep your goals in mind.

People who are positive, driven and in control make you become driven also, just by spending time around them, listening to them, watching how they take on the world. On the other hand if you surround yourself with negative, lazy people, no will power, no drive, then you too can become this way just as easily. You will start seeing the world in a negative way. So please choose who you surround yourself with wisely.

I want you to think of the top five people who you surround yourself with. Write down their names and think about them first before answering:

Are they hard working?
Do they have goals they want to achieve?
Do they support you in the decisions you make?
Do they laugh *with* you and not *at* you?

Answer these questions so you can have a clear view on the positive or negative people you are surrounding yourself with. *(Be honest with yourself.)*

Person 1.....................   Positive or Negative.....................

Person 2.....................   Positive or Negative.....................

Person 3.....................   Positive or Negative.....................

Person 4.....................   Positive or Negative.....................

Person 5.....................   Positive or Negative.....................

Being yourself

You now may think of the person you are as the person that

you are when around your friends or even around your family. However, I'm talking about something completely different. The person you are when you're with your friends – that's not the real you, that's a version of you that you want to be when around those people, right? I bet you happen to like what they like and want to do what they want to do. I'm also not talking about the type of person that you are around your family, I bet you're a much different person than you are with your friends.

In fact, I'm actually talking about the person you really are, the person you are when no one else is around to influence your choices or change your mind, when no one is around that you are trying to impress or trying to be like. The real you is when you are alone, so let's strip it right back for a second … let's find the real you …

I want you to think back to your first day in school. What type of person were you?

Cast your mind back to when you were standing in line surrounded by everyone in your class for the first time. Were you intimidated? Were you shy? Did you put your head down? Maybe you were the opposite, maybe you made friends instantly? Maybe you were the joker of the class or maybe you spoke too much and listened too little?

Finding out who we are when we are with the ones we love will tell us nothing about our character; however, finding out who we are when we are faced with situations out of our comfort zone will tell us exactly who we are and how we will handle situations we must face alone – just like competing in the World Irish Dance Championships!

This is truly the person you are; stepping outside of that comfort zone for the first time will show you the real you. If you are not happy or confident with how you feel out of your comfort zone don't worry, it is OK. *Reaching New Heights* is designed to build that confidence and shape the person you know you can be!

I want you to write it down, the real you:

The type of person I am: ....

....

....

Now, can you shout it out loud for me? Stand up and shout who the real you is. I want you to identify a label that tells you who you are. Live in alignment with your beliefs and morals, and establish your own identity, not a combination of the others around you; build courage, find focus and go in the direction that you want to go in.

Be honest with yourself about what type of person you are. Nothing's better than a happy, positive you. Not the cocky *(too big for your boots)* attitude we all adopt sometimes, but the confident person who is comfortable in their own skin and who doesn't care who likes or dislikes them because they are being themselves without anyone else changing their character. Is this type of person you?

This book is about developing you into the best you can be so we need to start by understanding your real characteristics so that we can build upon them. If you were shy, we will make you more confident. If you don't believe you have what it takes, I will prove to you that you do. If you are too loud, talk too much or lose focus, by the time you have read this book you will have listened more than you've spoken, so you will have changed something already, right?

Too many follow the crowd and become a version of those that they surround themselves with. Being a champion is a lonely journey. Others can walk the road with you, but they cannot walk it for you. You become your own best friend and you must be confident in who you are without needing others around you. Yes, it is great to get support along the way; however, you cannot take your friends onto that stage with you, you will take that walk alone – your confidence must shine, with or without them.

Be the person everyone wants to be around

Everyone loves being around a person who is happy, caring, confident, polite, and funny; they make everyone laugh out loud and feel good about themselves. Laughing is the best medicine for every human and if you can create it, it will be the best medicine for your success, too!

I want you to think of everyone in your dance class for a second. I bet there are some who will instantly make you feel happier when they come in, who will lift everyone's performance and keep you coming back to class. Then there will no doubt be others who instantly complain they're tired or that the training is too hard. They want a rest and they drag everyone else down by doing so. These people place doubt in your mind and make you question why you are coming to class in the first place; they make you think that there must be better things to do. The enjoyment is lost.

Being happy to others immediately makes you happy, lifting other dancers' performances will immediately raise your own performance. Each and every day I want you to be the person everyone wants to be around. Be that person everyone looks for walking into class. Say hi to everyone you meet, ask them how their day has been. Yes, they may look at you weirdly for a second, but that's only because no one ever asks them how their day has been. I mean, they aren't so important that others should care about their day, right? I bet that person walks away feeling better about themselves and that little bit more important that you actually took a moment to care about how they are or what their day has been like.

Telling someone their clothes are nice or they are looking well today will immediately boost that person's confidence. Ultimately that person got dressed today thinking they would probably not be noticed; noticing others gives them their place in this world and doing so confirms you have your place, too. Be that breath of fresh air, show everyone that we are all important and success in life will come much more easily to you.

Know what fuels your fire

As an athlete you need to know what makes you tick. Just like money makes a sales person thrive, knowing what fuels your fire is one of the simplest ways to drive your performance. Unfortunately many when asked do not know what it actually is that motivates them. As we are all different, we require different techniques and keys to help motivate ourselves. You will need to understand what helps your performance and what type of people you should be around to keep motivated. In Chapter 2 I have dedicated an entire section to motivation and laid out tasks that I hope will help you see and understand firstly how to get motivated and then what will keep you motivated along the way.

Shadow a mentor

What is a mentor?

A mentor can be a teacher, adviser, coach, a champion of their sport or a top dancer, past or present. They may be male or female, or a dance teacher who is much older than you.

A mentor is a person who you look up to and place your trust in, and who guides people who are less experienced. They show they are one hundred per cent committed to you, they are loyal and help teach you the best techniques and corrections they can so that you are headed in the right direction. Mentors are role models for you and are dependable; they want what is best for you; they are positive people to be around.

Why should we all have one?

I believe everyone should have a mentor from the get go. It is said to be one of the most crucial keys to success. A mentor has already been there and done it. They know the ins and outs, the good and bad points, they know what works and what doesn't work. A mentor is a person who will help you avoid failure the best way possible, help you figure a way around it so that you don't have to learn the hard way, a person that is willing to help you be the best person you can be and lead you on your road to success.

A mentor isn't your parent, as you are less likely to listen to their sporting advice. A mentor sees the potential in you that even you might not see, they bring the best out in you. They will have many contacts that you won't have, and this will help push your career forward. Having the contacts that your mentor has is priceless. For a free service, it is the best service you can ask for, you can even grow a strong friendship along the way. They might show you career paths that you have never heard of before. So why not have one?

By writing this book I am offering to be your mentor. I already see the potential each of you has and I will certainly bring out the best in you. *Reaching New Heights* is your mentor, it knows the ins and outs of becoming the best and already knows what works and what doesn't. It will help you avoid failure in the best possible way and be key on your road to success, Listen to it!

Never be afraid to ask for help

Don't sit quietly and think … what if? If you want to find out something, or you are bursting to ask a question, but the words won't come out because you're afraid of how that person will react, then take a deep breath or count to ten. What's the worst that can happen? We are all human. We are all the same. No one is better than anyone else, so why should you ever feel timid about asking for help from another human? How much further on would you be right now if you just asked that question and got your answer? You could be in that position one day and not realise you're helping others, too, when they want to know something and are afraid to ask. Little do you know you could be staring in the face of someone just like you once were, afraid of asking questions but really wanting the answers. Any question anyone asks always has an answer to it.

Every question is an important question, there is no such thing as a stupid question. Be brave, think positive thoughts, step out of your comfort zone and get the help and respect you deserve.

Over the past few years I have answered many questions that, even though they were aimed in the completely wrong direction, I did not laugh at or think were silly questions. Instead I answered as best I could so that person would not make the same mistake again. I know many others wanted to ask questions but didn't. I created podcasts and newsletters to answer the most popular questions and slowly others began to ask more and more. I know there are still more dancers out there with questions to ask. If this is you, write your question down, keep it with you throughout the book and if *Reaching New Heights* does not give you the answer, please contact me directly and I will be that person you need to answer your questions. Questions need answers!

Observe your competition

In order for you to know where you are, you must know where you need to get to, therefore you must see what is achievable and what you need to start to do to get there. You must compare your performance to others to allow you to know what you can do better. Take down notes about how your top competitors stand out. Is it their posture? Their walk on? Their overall dancing, with natural turn outs or over crossing? Whatever it may be, you need to take it all in so that you can be at a good level also. Think of why they got up there in the first place, why some dancers stand out much more than the others do.

Write down how they act at competition day: what do they do behind stage? What are they doing differently that you aren't doing? Watch how they practise and focus on getting in their positive mindset. Check out their Facebook page to see if they are giving away any tips on what they are doing, i.e. training outside of dancing.

Go up and chat to them, or email them. They are on top for a reason or they have been there and done it before you, so what is wrong with you finding out new ways to help you get higher results also? What is wrong with finding out how to avoid failure or bad memories? That's exactly why you are reading this book, right?

If observing your competition makes you nervous then I suggest you watch footage of your competition after the event is over.

Go for it, start to make your changes right now. If you want to be the best you can be, new changes have to be made right now. I'm here for you, so any help you may need tag me, email me!

Dress to your performance every day

Wake up every day and smile in the mirror, be happy, put on your best clothes, say hi to everyone, be positive, and this will become the person you are and make you feel great inside. Go into dance class and be well presented, with clean hard shoes and pumps; these shoes need to be respected like treasure.

Think about it … if you were to walk into a gym to choose a personal trainer, would you pick the trainer that had dirty shoes on, wrinkled clothes and was out of shape? Or the trainer dressed in neatly ironed clothes, clean shoes and who was in great condition? It's the principle of how you see yourself and feel good, and knowing how others see and judge you. Who doesn't feel great when putting effort into their appearance and clothing? Knowing you look good makes you feel good. It changes your mood into a loveable, positive, happy you. You rub off on others also, so people around you want to be around you more because you are making their day shine brighter.

I'm not saying go out and buy a whole new wardrobe, it's not about that, it's about looking the part; clean, tidy, presentable.

I promise you, it goes that extra mile to make you feel great all day long. Your performance comes out better, and you can feel this all happening inside you. Get up and dress to your performance each and every day!

'SOME JOURNEYS NEED TO BE TAKEN ALONE. IT IS ONLY THEN WILL WE FIND OUT WHO WE REALLY ARE.' — Lauren Early

---

CHAPTER SUMMARY

Important points to note:

- Surround yourself with likeminded friends who support your goals
- Be the REAL you
- Be the person everyone wants to be around
- Have a mentor
- Never be afraid to ask for help
- Observe your competition
- Dress to your performance every day

Chapter 2
Know what fuels your fire:
motivation, mindset and goal setting

Motivation is the drive and desire within us to achieve our personal goals. Many who have no goals in life often don't realise they also have no motivation; they also don't possess the mindset required to achieve. I have subtitled this chapter 'Motivation, Mindset and Goal Setting'. Why? Because you can't have one without the other two. If you have no goals, you do not have the proper mindset and you have no motivation; if you have no motivation you do not have the mindset to achieve any goals! However, laying out goals in life will create new motivation and you'll develop a champion's mindset along the way.

Too many people stop growing, they lose motivation, they stop wanting anything and they become satisfied with what they have. They are comfortable within their comfort zone and will go to work or school every day with only the weekend in sight as their target or goal. In life when you are not chasing a goal you are not living, you are merely going through each day without a purpose. Do you have a purpose? DO you have a reason to get out of bed? If not, why not?

Having a purpose in life will take us out of our comfort zone and on our way to achieving our goals. Once those goals are achieved we will realise that in the process of change we have discovered talents and abilities that we didn't even know we had. Unless you try to do something beyond what you have already done then you will never grow, but without a purpose or a goal you will never know.

Now is not the time to talk yourself out of it or to tell yourself you will do it some other time. Now is the time to pick that goal, find that purpose and drive that motivation. How many people have you heard saying on a Friday that they will start their new diet on Monday? They give themselves a full weekend of opportunity to eat and drink everything they want. Why? Because the easy option is to start on a Monday, the hard option is to start on a Friday. Now, how many of those people actually start their diet on Monday? And how many people see it through to the end? Exactly.

The secret to being a champion is that you already are a champion inside. You don't beg an average person to be phenomenal, you don't push an average person to be great, they already are great, they already are phenomenal, because they have a goal, the motivation, the mindset and a purpose in life.

Many people will read this book because they are not where they want to be. Let me tell you if you're not where you want to be, if you don't already have what you want to have, if you're not already where you think you should be, then there is a reason for this. It's not because the system has failed you or because of others, it is simply because you are not making the sacrifices necessary to get to where you want to be, you are lacking motivation, lacking a purpose and lacking a goal. I mean, even I would struggle to train hard every day if I didn't have a goal in mind. What would my purpose be? I want you to pick your goal and make it a reality, and I want to help you because if you don't, you will sit back and watch someone else make theirs a reality and at that point it is too late for you.

There are no such things as disadvantages. We all have the same opportunities, we are all faced with hurdles that stand in our way and we all have the same amount of time – the question is what are you going to do with your time? Many people work a job they don't want to be in and get through their day full of dreams and aspirations that are never acted upon.

Let me tell you that there is no secret to success. Many people go through life trying to find a quick way to get rich or a fast way to lose weight, and what they are really looking to find is an easy way through life. There are no secrets and there are no quick fixes. This book does not contain magic training methods or secret foods to eat. It contains basic facts and principles. These principles are not magic, but they are the keys to success. What people fail to understand is that success does not happen overnight. If applying these fundamental principles to your training does not make you a champion overnight, will you then blame this book for you giving up too soon?

The real secret lies in how long these principles need to be repeated for. Being a champion is a lot of small things done well over and over again. Workout after workout, meal after meal, day after day. There is no shortcut, there is no easy way. If anyone tells you there is, they are lying. A champion takes the basics and repeats them day in and day out until they reach their goal. They realise there is no elevator to success, but they don't care – they are willing to climb the stairs step by step until they reach the top. That's how a champion will spend their time!

Before we embark on your new goals I want you to acknowledge that the path in-front of you is not an easy one, but one that once walked will be worth every step. There are three words that I want you to write down and set beside your bed. These words should be the first thing that you look at when you wake up in the morning:

'DAY AFTER DAY'

These three words define a champion. Everyone wants the champion's spotlight; however, when they are faced with the reality of what it takes, many people slowly want it less and less. A true champion realises success is an accumulation of repeated efforts, day after day. Acknowledge that, accept that, realise what is ahead of you, and let's walk it together.

Your current motivation, mindset and goals

Before we begin the training sections of the book let's finally acknowledge what motivates us, what our goals are and how strong our mindset is to achieve these goals. It is only when we realise what we want from this book that the training sections will be of any use to us. We must go through this book with a clear goal to relate everything to.

I want you to write down what motivates you, and why

....

....

....

What are your goals?

....

....

....

What is your purpose in life?

....

....

....

I hope by now you truly understand the person you are, what you want to achieve in life and the dedication required to get you there. My reason for putting this section at the beginning of the book is that the best training in the world can't help you achieve your goals if you don't want it bad enough. Your mindset must come first!

Now that you understand the impact your mindset can have on your success in life let's move on to teaching you the training principles that will get you to the top.

I will leave you in the experienced hands of Robert McAvoy who will teach you everything you need to know about the correct training and nutrition principles required to become a World class athlete. Grab a pen and get ready to embrace the professional world of training and nutrition like you've never experienced before.

'A TRUE CHAMPION REALISES SUCESS IS AN ACCUMULATION OF REPEATED EFFORTS DAY AFTER DAY.' — Lauren Early

CHAPTER SUMMARY

Important points to note:

- **Stay outside your comfort zone**
- **There is no secret or shortcut to success**
- **We all have the same opportunities, disadvantages and time**
- **Have a purpose in life**
- **Have a goal**
- **Know what motivates you**
- **Adopt the right mindset to achieve your goals**

BELFAST - 2006

BELFAST - 2008

GLASGOW - 2007

World **6** Titles

DUBLIN - 2010

PHILADELPHIA - 2009

GLASGOW - 2011

PART 2

TRAINING FOR OPTIMAL DANCE PERFORMANCE

Overview

'Who is this book for?'

This book is a beginner's guide for anyone wishing to get a clear understanding of how to incorporate strength and conditioning training into their current training regime in an easy to use format, either to directly improve their own personal performance or as an aid in assisting current dance teachers / strength coaches to improve the performance of their dancers. This book is an entry level guide on how to improve the performance of Irish dancing; if this is of interest to you then this book is certainly for you and will not disappoint.

'Who is this book not for?'

If you are already incorporating the basics of strength and conditioning training into your current training regime / your dancers' training regime and are searching to learn for advanced coaching methods for dancers, then this book is not for you. The purpose of this book is to enhance performance at a basic level, which is all the sport needs at this stage. There will be intermediate and / or advanced guides written in the future, but only when I feel the dancing community has caught up and fully understands how to implement the basics of strength and performance [Q: performance, not conditioning?] training into their programmes. Only then will I consider teaching more advanced techniques, to ensure the sport keeps progressing while avoiding any confusion arising as a result of delivering too much information all at once.

What is a strength and conditioning coach?

A strength and conditioning (S&C) coach is a fitness professional whose primary role as a coach is to improve performance in athletic competition. The coach may also aid injury prevention and enforce proper movement patterns required for the given sport.

Whilst a personal trainer's client demographic is the general public, an S&C coach has a demographic of sport-specific athletes, therefore requires a more specific skill set.

The strength coach plays a specific role in improving performance and producing results for athletes in a broad range of sports, covering the movement patterns of running, jumping, agility, power, speed, endurance, coordination and much more. It is the S&C coach's job to work directly with the athlete and the athlete's sporting coach to develop programming to directly improve performance in relation to the specific sport and the movement patterns it requires of the athlete.

The coach must also take into consideration common injuries, periodisation of programmes for off season and in season training, and how to peak for certain competitions. The S&C coach must analyse the fundamental movement patterns of the sport and develop a programme to improve the technical abilities of the athlete and the specific strength qualities that underpin the movements.

Any athlete looking to reach a world class level should be working closely with a quality strength and conditioning coach and moving away from the generic fitness training approach that we too commonly see.

To show you just how much observation should be done by a coach prior to coaching an athlete in any given sport I have included a copy of my observation list below.

As a strength coach, when asked to train an athlete in any given sport I first attend a competition or training session to observe and monitor the movement patterns of their sport. This initial observation will tell me a lot about the sport. I will tend to look for the following key points:

OBSERVATION LIST
Team or Individual Sport
Movement Patterns
Primary Muscles Involved
Secondary Muscles Involved
Upper Body Requirements
Lower Body Requirements
Duration of the Event
Energy Systems Used
Impact / Non-Impact

Potential Injuries
Structural Balance Assessment
Core Involvement
Ideal Body Composition for Optimal Performance
Flexibility / Range of Movement Required
Off Season Duration
In Season Duration
Competition Frequency

From this initial observation and the information recorded I will have gained an extremely clear picture as to what qualities a top level athlete in this sport must have to reach the top.

Next I will sit down with the athlete and assess him / her in each of these areas to see how they match the requirements of the sport. Based on the assessment results I can develop a training programme specifically tailored to the requirements of both the sport and the individual athlete based on his / her current level of ability and identified weaknesses.

My Irish dance observations

In 2009 I was approached and asked to coach Lauren Early for an upcoming World Championships. Lauren had already won several world titles at a younger age; however, this one was different.

Lauren was then sixteen and as hormones change things no longer come as they once did. With body fat much easier to obtain and much harder to lose, more injuries from the build-up of years of training, and more pressure and expectation from being an existing world champion, she was ready to take her athletic ability to the next level but didn't quite know how.

Firstly it's important to note here that Lauren had a great dance set up and a teaching team that had developed her dance ability to a high level. However this, along with genetic ability, can only take an athlete so far.

Lauren was now ready to seek other ways to enhance her performance and during our initial consultation she discussed her disappointment at the lack of support for a world champion outside of the weekly dance classes she attended.

Despite the many types of athletes I had trained, before that point I had never coached an Irish dancer. After our initial consultation I was also quite shocked to find out that a multiple time world champion has no opportunity for funding, no opportunity for paid strength coaching, and no nutrition or injury support. Comparing this to government-backed sports, where all these opportunities are provided to their top athletes for free, I realised that Irish dancing was quite a bit behind other sports and also quite disadvantaged with regard to outside support.

I asked to join Lauren at her next local competition to enable me to complete my observation list to allow me to gather the information I required. Here are my findings:

OBSERVATION LIST	OBSERVATION FINDINGS
Team or Individual Sport	Individual (except team dances)
Movement Patterns	Multidirectional
Primary Muscles Involved	Quadriceps / Calves / Hip flexors
Secondary Muscles Involved	Hamstrings / Abductors / Upper body & Core stabilisers
Upper Body Requirements	Static upper body with retracted shoulder blades
Lower Body Requirements	Sharp single leg movements requiring take off & landing
Duration of the Event	40-60 seconds – up to 3 rounds with ample recovery time in between
Energy Systems Used	Anaerobic lactic system
Impact / Non-Impact	Impact on ground landing
Potential Injuries	Hamstrings / Shins / Calves / Knees / Ankles / Hips
Structural Balance Assessment	Full lower body structural balance required
Core Involvement	Strong core / back stability required for upper body
Ideal Body Composition for Optimal Performance	Female 18-22% bf male 10-13% bf
Flexibility / Mobility Range of Movement Required	Full range of motion in hips required, good level of hip and hamstring flexibility required, but small degree of tightness also required for elastic strength of muscle
Off Season Duration	May-August
In Season Duration	September-April
Competition Frequency	8-12 competitions

As you can see, above are my findings from when I first observed the sport. This then gave me the relevant information required to create world class programming based on the fundamental requirements of Irish dancing.

It is my professional opinion that any coach or trainer who is prescribing training programmes without first going through the above process or already having experience within the sport is going to deliver sub-par results, because they have not taken the time to analyse the sport or the requirements of the athlete.

If anyone has ever hired a trainer who has no specific experience in teaching Irish dance athletes, no experience with dance themselves, or no study knowledge of the mechanics of the sport, they have been short-changed. Prior to beginning your training, the trainer should have observed a competition or one of your training sessions and compiled an observation list on the sport. To prescribe programmes for dancers without ever analysing the sport is poor quality coaching and questions must be asked about how specific the training is to your needs and your sport – isn't this just general fitness training that is being perceived to be for Irish dance?

This is the difference between training the public for general fitness by prescribing blanket exercise programmes and training an athlete for a specific sport – every movement must be analysed and every programme must be tailored to the athlete's current ability.

Final word

Irish dancing is a competitive sport that reaches out across many countries and competes to the highest level with an annual World Championships. As Irish dancing is a private sport and not publicly backed or funded, the sport has very few resources outside of what we provide ourselves, therefore we simply won't have any great coaching set ups unless we create them. This is hopefully where this book, along with our continued support of your training, will make a difference. It will positively address the lack of resources available for strength training in Irish dancing so that you can, as athletes, finally feel that you are part of a sport.

Robert McAvoy

Chapter 3

Adopting the correct training approach: aerobic vs anaerobic

Overview

Firstly let's determine the fundamental differences between exercise and sport-specific training:

Exercise

Ongoing exercise is when a person has no progression structure, training plans, start or end goals and no real nutrition structure to back up the exercise. The person will exercise within their comfort zone, enjoy the endorphin release and the feel good factor of attending the gym and ticking the box each time they finish a session. The exercises selected will be those that the person feels most comfortable doing, regardless of the outcome or benefits the exercise brings in relation to their goals. After a period of six or twelve months when they come around and look in the mirror or check their progress they see that nothing much has changed. Their body has adapted to the training stimulus placed upon it as each session is very similar to the one that came before it and the one to come next.

This group will generally be made up of people that take part in sports as a hobby but don't intend to compete at a high level, and eighty-five per cent of general gym users.

Sport-specific training

The person or athlete will have outlined goals and set timeframes within which those goals should be achieved. There will be structured training plans to be completed, with consistent overload of the body to ensure progression occurs. A fully tailored nutrition plan will complement the training plan(s). The training involved will be carefully chosen to match the movement patterns of their specific sport and reduce risk of injury. When the timeframe is completed assessments will be conducted to show progression and the changes that have occurred since the athlete / dancer started before making alterations and setting a new training programme in place for the next phase. The athlete will have a coaching network made up of the coach in charge of the sport, as well as a strength and conditioning coach in charge of training and programming.

This group will make up the majority of athletes in the world's top sports that have a professional level to aim for, and a small percentage of gym users in the general population.

As a competitive Irish dancer, which group do you feel that you are currently in? For those of you who are completing extra fitness work inside or outside of dance class, do you feel the training is structured around general exercise or specific to your dancing needs? Maybe you already have a trainer; has this trainer any experience in dancing requirements, and is your trainer logging all of your progression? Can you go back and ask for your training logs from when you first started or are no records kept? If not, why not?

Getting fit

The fundamental reason we exercise is to get fitter, right? But what is fitness?

There are many different variables of fitness. We would all say a marathon runner is fit, and at the same time we would say a sprinter is also fit. Both are, in fact, extremely 'fit' athletes; however, the fundamental components of their fitness are totally different.

One athlete is required to be fit so they can last a long period of time and the other is required to be fit to be able to produce force, power and speed over a short distance.

If either athlete was to get their style of training wrong it would hamper their performance.

Unfortunately we see a very high percentage of dancers completing the wrong type of fitness for their sport and so little progression is made. I will explain more about the different types of fitness training and which is best for our sport later in this chapter. For now just consider the type of fitness training you complete and whether it is actually the correct fitness work required by our sport.

Is dancing a sport or a performance?

Because dancing is best known as a performance rather than as a sport there is a huge lack of knowledge and research about how to train a dancer for high level performance. If we look at dance as a whole the majority of the different types of dancing are non-competitive and for this reason I believe researchers have always skipped studying dancing for more competitive sports. Up until now we have simply been guessing as to what the best way to train actually is.

In my opinion any athlete who is a competitor is not a performer and therefore if you are a competitive Irish dancer then Irish dancing should be treated as a sport.

It is my aim in the next chapter to collect together the little research that I have found along with my own analysis of the sport to teach you the most optimal way to train for competitive Irish dance.

Energy systems used in sport and exercise

Understanding the energy systems that the human body operates from helps us to understand what fuel system we use for different types of activities. It is important as athletes we understand firstly what type of energy pathway our body uses during a competition and secondly how we go about training that energy system in class to improve our output and drive performance. This chapter outlines three main energy systems used and their relevance in different sports including Irish dancing.

Let me begin by having a look at the energy requirements in all sports and the different energy systems we use depending on the duration of the sports requirements. I must make it clear that the body will not solely use one fuel system, but rather it will use a mixture of several as time goes on. It is important we know which energy system our body uses in Irish dancing so that we can ensure what we use in our training is similar to that which we use in competition. Why train like a marathon runner if you want to sprint, right?

Firstly let's break it down into two groups:

Aerobic exercise

The body exercises in a steady controlled state, long and moderate enough for oxygen to be present and carbon dioxide to be produced.

This type of exercise would be prevalent in long distance sports such as marathon running. Aerobic exercise typically consists of slow, robotic actions that continue for a long period of time. It usually will not include any powerful jumps, explosive movements or sharp turns requiring maximal effort, and for this reason aerobic exercise uses mostly our slow twitch muscle fibres *(more on muscle fibres later)*.

If competing in an aerobic sport the athlete must ensure training their aerobic system is a priority and structure their class training accordingly. In other words, it would be much more beneficial for the athlete to train over longer periods, with short or no rest periods, similar to the competition requirements.

Anaerobic exercise

The body exercises at a fast, aggressive pace, the output will be faster than the speed at which the body can get oxygen in therefore with no oxygen present lactic acid will be produced. Anaerobic exercise would be prevalent in sports such as sprinting and, of course, competitive Irish dancing.

If competing in an anaerobic sport, the athlete must make anaerobic training a priority and structure their class training accordingly. Because of the fast-paced nature of anaerobic sports they mostly use their fast twitch muscle fibres, therefore it would be much more beneficial for the athlete to train with short and intense bursts of speed, power and aggression, taking longer rest periods to ensure the intensity can be kept high, again similar to competition conditions.

There are also some sports that will require the use of both systems. Football, for example, lasts a long period of time, and yet short bursts of speed are also required. This means that when planning sport-specific training a footballer would incorporate both aerobic and anaerobic exercise into his programme.

Energy pathways used in sport and exercise

Now that we know the differences between aerobic and anaerobic exercise we will briefly look at what fuel system each of the two uses, and the duration of usage.

Below is a table showing the different energy systems and the duration of exercise they are applicable to:

ENERGY SYSTEM	ACTIVITY LENGTH	ACTIVITY INTENSITY	BENIFITS	DRAWBACKS
Anaerobic *(lactic system)*	0-15 secs	Maximum Effort	Improved heart function Decreased body fat Increased muscle mass Increased strength Increased speed Increased power	Requires aerobic base foundation

Anaerobic (lactic system)	15 secs-2 minutes	High Intensity	Improved heart function Decreased body fat Increased muscle mass Increased strength Increased speed Increased power	Requires aerobic base foundation
Aerobic (carbon dioxide)	2 minutes +	Low Intensity	Improved heart function Improved lung capacity VO2 max Decreased body fat	Loss of muscle mass Loss of strength Loss of speed Loss of power

* Table showing the different requirements of fuel systems over different periods of time

The above table shows all three energy systems, their duration, activity level, benefits and drawbacks.

1. In the first row we see the **anaerobic system** is used in sports requiring bursts of power and speed up to fifteen seconds, such as a 100 metre race. The benefits improving this area confers include higher intensity, improved speed, greater power, more strength, increased muscle mass and decreased body fat.

2. In the second row we see the **anaerobic lactic acid system** used in sports requiring up to two minutes of speed, such as a 400 metre race, and in our case this is where competitive

Irish dance would fit in. The benefits improving this area confers are again higher intensity, improved speed, greater power, more strength, increased muscle mass and decreased body fat. We will also improve our ability to tolerate the build-up of lactic acid by training in this zone.

3. In the third row we see the **aerobic system,** for use in long distance sports. The intensity level is low to allow the athlete to continue for a long period of time, anything from two minutes right up-to several hours, as would be the case with a marathon runner. The benefits that training the aerobic system confers are improved heart function and improved VO_2 max (maximal aerobic capacity); however, the downside to developing great aerobic ability is the loss of speed, muscle mass, power and strength.

It is not possible to develop all three areas maximally. We can be average at all three or be great at one. Developing one will always take away from the others. For the general public this may not be a problem, as to be an all-rounder, being reasonably fit as well as reasonably strong is possible. However, being extremely sharp and powerful along with being extremely aerobic is just not possible. Why?

Improving your VO_2 max, your ability to last for longer, will actually reduce your speed, power, strength and your vertical jump. This happens as our fast twitch muscle fibres are recruited to act like a slow twitch muscle fibre to aid in your aerobic training, hence the loss of the speed based qualities. You only have to look at a marathon runner's physique compared to that of a sprinter to see how much muscle and strength loss a marathon runner will experience by completing long bouts of aerobic activity.

The sacrifice of muscle mass and strength is acceptable for a marathon runner, given the requirement of that sport is to run for long distances where little speed and strength are required. This, however, would not be such a great trade-off for an Irish dancer, who would not want to sacrifice their speed, power, strength and vertical jump all at the expense of improving their endurance fitness levels. You only need to dance for one to two minutes, remember what is more important on stage.

From a dancer's perspective we firstly need to know which fuel system we use to give us the best chance of improving our performance. The fundamental components that make up a great dancer, as we just mentioned, are speed, power, sharpness, acceleration, strength, a low percentage of body fat, and the ability to tolerate high levels of lactic acid. Our event time is around forty-five seconds to two minutes in duration. If we refer all these details back up into our energy systems chart we will see that once we match Irish dancing requirements to the necessary fuel system we fall firmly into the second row.

This means the main fuel system Irish dancers will use most during competition will be the **anaerobic lactic system. Please**

note this down.

I mentioned at the start the body will not solely use one fuel system; however, the percentage of which fuel system we use will give us the best insight into how best to structure our training.

Below is a table I have illustrated to give an estimation of the percentage of energy system usage in different athletic events.

Sport	Aerobic Fuel System	Anaerobic Fuel System
Marathon	90%	10%
1500m	50%	50%
400m sprint	20%	80%
100m sprint	10%	90%

* Estimation table showing energy pathways relative to distance and time completed

Look at the trend I have demonstrated in the example. As the distance goes up, so too does the use of the **aerobic system**. As the distance goes down, the speed goes up and so too does the use of the **anaerobic system**.

1. In the first row we see a marathon runner may use **90% aerobic and only 10% anaerobic** energy. Knowing this, as a marathon runner I would want to spend 90% of my training sessions in the aerobic zone and only 10% in the anaerobic zone to match the requirements of my sport.

2. In the second row we see a 1500 metre runner may use **50% aerobic and 50% anaerobic** energy. Knowing this, as a 1500 metre runner I would want to spend around half of my time training in the aerobic zone and half of my training would be completed in the anaerobic zone.

3. In the third row we see a 400 metre runner may use only **20% aerobic and 80% anaerobic** energy. Knowing this, as a 400 metre runner I would want to spend only 20% of my time training in the aerobic zone and 80% of my training would be completed in the anaerobic zone.

4. In the third row we see a 100 metre runner may use only **10% aerobic and 90% anaerobic** energy. Knowing this, as a 100 metre runner I would want to spend only 10% of my time training in the aerobic zone and 80% of my training should be completed in the anaerobic zone.

Of course Irish dancing has never been researched to this extent. However, we know enough to compare the duration of our event to that of a 400 metre sprint. It has similar requirements of speed, power and sharpness, and a similar lactic acid build up, as well as roughly the same time duration per event. *(Forty-five seconds to two minutes.) Please see option number 3.*

Now it becomes clear that as dancers, if we spend one hundred per cent of our time training the aerobic energy system it may only be able to benefit twenty per cent of our dance performance! However if we were to spend one hundred per cent of our time training the anaerobic system, it may be able to benefit our performance by eighty per cent.

Ever feel like you're training very hard and getting nowhere? You may want to check which energy system you are training.

Intensity vs volume relationship

Overview

There is an inverse relationship between **intensity** and **volume.** As **intensity** rises, **volume** must drop. The opposite is also true; as **volume** rises, the **intensity** must drop to allow for more **volume**.

In other words, as your speed and power increase, the distance and time you last for must decrease.

> **'As speed and power increase, distance and
> time must decrease'**

Why can't we be great at both speed based and endurance based sports? Why can't we be sharp and powerful dancers and keep this going for long periods of time?

You cannot have high intensity and high volume at the same time. If this was possible every marathon runner would be running the race at the same pace as a 100 metre race!

In order to dance for one hour the speed and power at which you dance must be reduced.

And in order to dance with one hundred per cent intensity, the duration must be reduced before the body loses its power and speed.

The human body is very smart. It will firstly determine how long it needs to do something for, before deciding how much intensity it can give to it. Your body will average out the intensity to ensure you last the duration.

If we train to improve our speed, our endurance will suffer and if we train our endurance, it will be at the expense of our speed. If we train both we will be average at both, but we can only be great at one. I hope that by now you're starting to have a clear picture as to which one is more important for our needs. More on this later.

I want you to remember the following take home points:

1. If I improve my VO_2 max greatly, my speed and strength will reduce.

2. If I improve my speed and strength greatly, my VO_2 max will reduce.

Fast twitch muscle fibres vs slow twitch muscle fibres

Genetically speaking, some of us are born with a higher percentage of fast twitch muscle fibres and others are born with a higher percentage of slow twitch muscle fibres. Most of us, however, are born with an average of both fibres and we are very capable of improving our performance if we focus our training according to the requirements of our sport. Using the same examples as above, there is little benefit in me spending the majority of my training time improving my speed *(fast twitch fibres)* if I want to be a marathon runner and require a great deal of endurance *(slow twitch fibres)*, and the reverse is also true.

There are three categories of muscle fibres:

1. Type 1 – Slow Twitch
2. Type 2a – Fast Twitch A
3. Type 2b – Fast Twitch B

Fast twitch muscle fibres are responsible for producing explosive power and sharpness with fast reaction times.

A well trained dancer should be able to react in a split second and be at optimal speed over a very short distance in a very short space of time. Whilst they are able to produce a lot of force and power, fast twitch muscles are not designed to last for long periods of time and therefore will only work over shorter distances.

Slow twitch muscle fibres have the opposite job; they are responsible for cyclical (repeated) movements over a long distance. They organise muscle contractions in quite a slow manner. As the aim is to last for long periods of time, slow twitch muscle fibres will not want to expend a lot of energy and therefore will not complete any fast, powerful movements that would expend a great deal of energy at once.

This would explain why if you take a dancer who is a predominately slow twitch athlete or has been completing a lot of aerobic work, such as distance running, outside of class, it will take a while to actually see some improvements in their speed or power. A distance athlete's body and brain are so used to using slow, cyclical movements that it will take some time and effort to actually learn how to react quickly, accelerate, and achieve top speed over a short distance.

Distance athletes switching to speed and strength training tend to find it initially quite easy, as their body has not learnt how to produce a significant amount of power or force in such a short space of time.

An example of this would be to take a marathon runner and get them to run 100 metres. They would be so slow off the mark that by the time they reached 100 metres very little speed would have been created, therefore they would find it quite easy. The more power and speed you can develop, the quicker the muscle will fatigue.

It's a great tip for all those of you who, after reading this book, switch from completing aerobic training to more of a sprint and strength training programme: remember that it may take a while to teach your body how to develop any real speed or power. This is due to your history of working your slow twitch muscle fibres. Be patient, though, as it will come. Eventually you will start to develop your fast twitch fibres again. In my experience you should begin to see an improvement in your reaction times and acceleration times over a period of six to ten weeks.

Beginner level athletes need not worry too much about muscle fibre usage. Whilst it is important to know there are differences, if you just ensure you are completing the right type of training - the muscle fibres will take care of themselves!

Power to weight ratio

The vertical jump, accelerating across the stage, the hop and the high kicks, are movements in which an Irish dancer will exert a sudden, rapid contraction against a load that may be challenging. The load in this case is their own body weight. The greater the body weight, the harder a job the body will have to exert a sudden contraction to move this weight in the direction we want and at the pace we would like, i.e. in the case of a vertical hop or jump.

Many dancers contact me looking to improve their speed, sharpness and acceleration skills. Whilst introducing speed and strength training would certainly help you to overcome your body weight more efficiently, there is one quicker and often over looked method to improve your speed.

Improving your power to weight ratio will automatically improve your acceleration speed, vertical jump, lift off the ground and reaction times without even specifically completing any direct speed or strength training.

For dancers that are not currently at optimal body fat levels, you are asking more of your body than those with a lower power to weight ratio, presenting yourself with a massive disadvantage.

What does power to weight ratio actually mean?

I want you to think of a Formula One (F1) car. This car has the perfect power to weight ratio, there are no parts on the car that are not necessary and the existing parts are all made out of the lightest material possible – this is all to enable the car to have a lighter power to weight ratio.

If we take the same engine as the F1 car but put it in a truck with much heavier parts, it will be nowhere near as fast. Even though the engine still has the same top speed capabilities, the load that it is being asked to move has now became greater, meaning the power to weight ratio has decreased and therefore the speed will also have to be reduced.

The human body is exactly the same. As a competitive Irish dancer you want to be on that stage with the most efficient power to weight ratio possible. It may not be necessary to stay at your optimal competition weight all year round; however, ensuring you are at the correct body fat percentage come competition time is crucial to your success. Ultimately you want to give yourself the best chance possible, right?

I am about to show you just how important being at your optimal power to weight ratio is to achieving your top performance.

The 100 metre test

Both myself and Lauren decided to conduct a recorded test to show just how important it is for a dancer's performance that they be at their ideal body weight come competition time.

If you would like to watch this test it can be found online on the 'Lauren Early' YouTube page under the name 'The 100m Test'.

The aim of the test was simple. Lauren was to complete 100

metres as fast as she could with just her own body weight and I would record the results and time.

After sufficient rest she would then attach a fourteen pound weighted vest and complete the 100 metres as fast as she could again. I would again record the results and time, and compare them with the first test.

On the morning of the test I weighed Lauren and she was 127lbs (58kg). This was roughly her competition weight from previous years, and judging by body fat levels she was lean enough to be in and around her optimal power to weight ratio for the test to be accurate.

Lauren and I went to the local athletics track with nothing but a stopwatch and a weighted vest, weighing fourteen pounds.

The recovery time given between each run was five minutes, long enough to ensure there was no fatigue still lingering from the previous run. She was fresh and fully recovered going into the second sprint.

The difference in results was astounding.

Lauren completed the first 100 metre run, at her bodyweight of 127lbs / 58kg, in **15.3** seconds.

The second 100 metre run, with Lauren carrying the additional

14lbs / 6.3kg, took **19.2** seconds to complete.

As you can see the time difference between runs was almost **4 seconds**.

This reduction in speed and power was due to Lauren carrying an extra fourteen pounds of unnecessary weight. This reduced her power to weight ratio massively.

Of course there are many different factors to consider when moving from a track onto a dance stage. However, this test only lasted 15-19 seconds. Bear in mind a competitive dance round lasts much longer, meaning the actual speed and power reduction could be greater than what was recorded here.

For all you dieters out there, this does not mean that you need to immediately go on a crash diet and be ultra-light with zero energy left to dance. I am simply showing the importance of achieving a comfortable weight that is not detrimental to your speed and power production. More on this in the nutrition sections.

Current level of fitness training for Irish dancers

Only over the last few years has extra fitness training become so popular with Irish dancers. Until recent years dancing was seen as a performing art; however, some dancers began to realise the benefits that extra fitness training could bring. Recently we have seen a surge of fitness training being included outside of class, and while it is great to see dancers taking the initiative to include extra work, unfortunately the exercise being completed lacks direction and structure.

I have witnessed many dancers completing three to five kilometre runs weekly to improve their fitness for dancing. I have also heard of dancers cycling many kilometres each week, also to improve stamina and fitness. One of the worst examples I have come across was when, during a consultation with a dancer, she told me she was cycling in an oxygen chamber for one hour, three times per week, to improve her fitness and VO_2 max. Her question to me was, 'Why am I not improving?'

This influx of fitness training then carried over into the dance class. More and more teachers began including fitness classes, completing a range of aerobic activity such as the burpee, squats and other fitness exercises.

On top of that we have seen the introduction of fitness trainers with little experience or knowledge of Irish dancing who come in and take classes with dancers – mostly aerobic fitness classes with very little sport specific exercise in place.

By now we should know the difference between aerobic training and anaerobic training inside out. We also know that completing aerobic work such as long distance running, cycling and hour long aerobic fitness classes may only benefit our performance up to twenty per cent.

Even though I have explained the differences, many dancers and teachers still fail to grasp the concept that aerobic training can actually be a disadvantage to the dancer. Ultimately it is common knowledge to assume that any training is good training and going to benefit us. Unfortunately that is not the case. Too commonly coaches and teachers figure that training equals results regardless of factoring in the type of training and the uniqueness of the dancer and the event.

One of the problems with class fitness training and aerobic training is that it will produce very little lactic acid. Therefore even though that dancer may be training hard, once they step on stage and experience the lactic acid build-up, their performance will very quickly suffer as the body does not know how to tolerate this waste product. It has not experienced this effect during training.

Group training

Even though competitive dance is an individual sport we tend to see the same programme being given out or completed by a mass of dancers. Regardless of their height, weight, gender, age or injury background, everyone in the class is completing all of the same training. How can an overweight dancer require the same exercises as an underweight dancer? How can a male dancer require the same as a female? Or how could a previously injured dancer require the same training as a dancer who is injury free? There is no individualisation of fitness training, even though dancing is an individual sport. Are we giving everyone the same training programme in the hope that it works for some?

Let's consider how this could happen.

The law of averages

The law of averages is also known as the law of numbers. To simply explain, the law of averages means that for every action you perform there will be a similar reaction or result, given a large enough sample. The law of averages dictates the expectation that a possible event or result is bound to happen, given enough repeated efforts in a large enough sample group.

Let's look at a few examples.

The law of averages dictates that if we have many rainy days then there is bound to be a sunny day soon. It also dictates that if we flip a coin one hundred times it will land on each side exactly the same amount of times.

What does this mean for me as a coach?

Example 1 – If I take a fitness class of fifty people, the law of averages states that I am bound to get results for a few people regardless of whether the training is suited to everyone.

Example 2 – If I take all my clients and give them the same training programme regardless of age, gender, weight, height, background and goals, I am still bound to produce results with a small number of them because for some of them it will happen to be what they need, although for others it might be the complete opposite.

What does this mean to you, the dancers and dance teachers?

In dancing terms, if I have a class of one hundred dancers and I have them all complete general fitness training three times per week, inside or outside of class, the law of averages states that at least a handful of the group will get results.

Say that several months after incorporating fitness training into class we see massively improved competition results in four of our dancers out of the one hundred; as a teacher would I view this as a success?

It would be human nature to think of this as a success, I agree; however, if we access this purely from a numbers perspective, the fitness training would have given a four per cent success rate with a ninety-six per cent fail rate. Only four people showed a marked improvement and ninety-six others showed no significant changes or improvements from the programme. See the trend?

As an external coach to athletes in many different sports it is my job to get a one hundred per cent success rate. If I train one hundred athletes in individual sports and only produce four quality athletes, then I have a ninety-six per cent fail rate.

As a dance teacher it is possible that every single one of your dancers gets results, given the training is specific enough to the individual. If the dancers are underachieving, getting injured or experiencing slow improvements, and individualised programming has not been given, then poor coaching is at fault.

It would have been very easy for Lauren to write a book showing you all the training she has done over the years to make her a champion and letting you follow her exact plans. The reason she has not done this is because her training worked for her, not you. You are different, you require a different approach. It is much more beneficial for you all to learn how to adapt training for your own body type than it would be for you to follow Lauren's or anyone else's training programmes.

Simply put, giving a dancer the same training that a champion is doing will not make that dancer a champion – but giving that dancer the correct training, specific to their own body type, can.

Group exercise and injuries

Giving the same training to a group of athletes will produce small results, but there will be many others who just won't respond or, worse, get injured. If your class is made up of different ages, different weights and different genders then all this must be taken into consideration when providing your dancers with training programmes. An overweight dancer would not require the same type of training as a dancer at their optimal weight, and the same goes for an underweight dancer.

I have provided an example of this scenario below

If I'm making a group of dancers complete a fitness circuit of jumping jacks and burpees (impact based exercises), then:

Dancer 1 – The overweight dancer will not be able to complete these efficiently and due to the extra weight will be putting way too much pressure through her joints, undoubtedly leading to stress related injuries that usually last a long time.

Dancer 2 – The optimal body weight dancer would be fine to complete the exercises given her great power to weight ratio.

Dancer 3 – Finally, the underweight dancer shouldn't be completing any extra training until her body is well nourished, fuelled and ready to recover efficiently, otherwise she will become overtrained and again, develop long lasting injuries.

By simply comparing the weight of three dancers across one simple exercise I hope you can already see the difference and changes that you would need to consider when prescribing class based exercise, and how you are putting many dancers at risk of possible injuries, not to mention those who have a previous history of injuries.

Another important factor to note is that the movements completed in training must be similar to the movement patterns required by the sport to actually cross over and have a benefit for performance. A great example would be the push up. Group fitness classes tend to have a mix of upper and lower body exercises. Let's say we include a push up as one of the exercises in our fitness class.

Whilst at first it might be hard for the dancer to complete one push up, if after six weeks they can complete ten push ups in class then that is a definite improvement in their upper body strength, right?

Now, do you think this improvement will help to improve their dance performance? Unfortunately there is no correlation between a push up and competitive dance movements, therefore this would be of very little benefit. We must ensure that the exercises we complete both in class and outside of class are actually similar to the movement patters of dancing, otherwise even though we are training hard there will be very little improvement in dance performance. Sometimes in sport training hard is not the answer – you have to train smart!

Final word

We only have to look at the extremely high injury rate of Irish dancers to see that these are real issues that need attention and individualised changes. If conducting group exercise classes, you must be very careful to plan the session to meet the needs of Irish dance and the requirements of each dancer, otherwise it just becomes the kind of group fitness that we would find at our local gym. Group fitness improves our aerobic capacity, but as athletes we need sport-specific training. Whether this is completed as a group or an individual it must be specific to the demands of an Irish dancer and mimic stage competition.

If this all sounds confusing to you, don't worry, it should. It's not your job to be a strength coach if you are not qualified, your job is to be a dance coach, a parent or a dancer, which I have no doubt you are all great at.

Do not panic if all this is new to you or after what you have been reading you now realise that you have been doing certain things wrong. Finding out what you have been doing wrong is the exact reason we wrote *Reaching New Heights*. It will help us all find a common ground, a platform that we can all work from. If you have been doing a lot of training different to the way I have described, just acknowledge it and be excited that everything is about to change. Remember, up until now you have all done the best you could given the little help you have had, so just imagine how much your performance is ready to change when you start to do everything right!

Are you ready to find out how to start training like a proper athlete?

'SOMETIMES IN SPORT TRAINING HARD IS NOT THE ANSWER – YOU HAVE TO TRAIN SMART.' – Lauren Early

---

CHAPTER SUMMARY

Important points to note:

- Dancing is mostly an anaerobic sport
- Completing too much aerobic work will decrease speed and power
- Use the 80% / 20% rule – for optimal dance performance train mostly with the anaerobic system, although a small portion of your training can be aerobic work in the off season to create a solid foundation
- Fitness training must include movements that replicate those of Irish dancing mechanics
- Focus on more intensity in your training, allow longer recovery periods and avoid volume with little rest periods
- As a competitive Irish dancer you use predominately fast twitch muscle fibres

Chapter 4

Adopting the correct training phases: off season – pre-season – in season

Behind every great athlete there is a great coach, behind every great coach there is great programming.

Periodisation

Periodisation is the systematic planning of athletic or physical training. [1] The aim is to reach your best possible performance for the most important competition of the year. [2] It involves progressive cycling of various aspects of a training programme during a specific period. Conditioning programmes can use periodisation to break up the training programme into the off season, pre-season, in season and postseason, or rest phase. Periodisation divides the year round conditioning programme into phases of training which focus on different goals. [3]

Periodisation for Irish dancers

One of the great benefits of periodisation is the breaking down of a dancer's training into different phases. Each training phase brings in a new training goal to work towards so that even if a competition is several months away, it still holds the dancer accountable at times when slacking off is likely.

Dancing as we currently know it has no existing structure or systematic planning of training phases. What we tend to see is Irish dancers completing the same type of training year round with the aim of being at their best most of the year. Science tells us this just isn't possible without experiencing a plateau in performance or injury occurring.

The importance of cycling different aspects of a training programme over different phases gives the dancer a specific target to work towards. This can be largely beneficial through times where the dancer has no competition for several months.

What is the main reason why we must change are training programmes?

The human body will adapt to the same training stimulus given we repeat it a set number of times. In other words a training programme is only as good as the length of time it takes your body to adapt to it. [13] Once this adaptation has occurred the programme will offer diminishing returns. The misleading part about this is that the programme can still technically feel hard, even when results have slowed.

In my experience you will have adapted to the same training after around four to eight sessions. I have found beginner athletes will be at the higher end and the more experienced athlete will be at the lower end of that scale. I have also seen Olympic level athletes adapt to training programmes in fewer than four sessions due to their body being so efficient.

This shows us that the more highly trained you are the quicker your body will adapt. Changes in programming don't have to be huge; simply slightly altering the distance, training time, weight used or the angle of the exercise will change the stimulus.

Given a dancer will be relatively new to any additional strength or speed training I would recommend the dancer changes their style of training every six to eight sessions. *(Six to eight weeks if the dancer is completing one strength or one speed session per week.)*

So far I have only spoken about adaptation to external training types, such as strength or sprint training; however, if we apply it to dance class the same adaptation rules would still apply. Having observed dance training in many different schools around the world, the one thing they all have in common is the lack of variability and regular changes in their training.

The current coaching set up tends to see dance schools complete the same training each week, year round, with the only changes being made as they come closer to competition season – and even then those changes are usually just an increase in volume of the same training, longer classes or extra days added in. This repetitive training pattern will almost certainly lead to small progressions in the dancer's performance, progress will plateau and the chance of injury will be raised significantly.

More of the same does not necessarily mean more results – in fact it can sometimes lead to slower progress as the body will adapt quicker.

If a dancer attends four classes per week, how beneficial do you think adding a fifth dance class would actually be if it is exactly the same as the other four? Is there any variance in your dance classes from one night to the next, or is each class based around the same layout?

I'm not saying we shouldn't train five days per week; however, five days of repeating the same training will give very little returns. On the other hand if we were to add in a fifth session but change the type of session it is, it would more than likely yield much greater results as it is new to the body.

For example if you dance four times per week and you want to improve your performance, instead of adding in a fifth class why not add in one day of sprint training per week, or one day of strength training? Even though this is only one extra day, the type of training is completely new to the body and therefore progress will be much greater than adding in a fifth dance class.

I have demonstrated how true this is with many dancers before. Here is an overview of an experiment I conducted in 2013 and its results.

Irish dance experiment

In 2013 I completed a training experiment with a dancer who, despite her best efforts, was seriously struggling to improve her performance. The dancer had trained four times a week for the previous three years, as well as completing two to three home practices each week. Her performance and placings were declining each year, injuries were increasing and motivation was lacking. The type of dance practice she did both in class and at home were exactly the same and nothing much had changed over the years in terms of the actual dance training being completed. Whilst the dance training was of a great standard, it was generally the same layout, same duration, same rest periods and the same intensity of training in each session. Both teacher and dancer knew that the dance training was correct and that her efforts in class were as good as they could be, so they were struggling to understand why progress had stagnated as new dancers in the class were progressing. *(Law of averages.)*

Overview of experiment

My experiment was to take a dancer away from class and not allow her to complete any dancing for four weeks either at class or at home. Within the four week period we would train different fundamental areas that would improve her performance, such as sprinting, strength training and structural balance exercises, all of which would have a positive carry-over into her dance performance.

Background information

We began the four weeks by completing some basic fitness tests around speed, strength and endurance to establish a baseline of where the dancer was in all these areas at this time. Once we had recorded the results we then began the four week training program.

My aim was simple – to do the opposite of everything she had been doing, in order to shock the body.

Her last three years of training had been high volume, too many classes per week and practice lasted for two to three hours. I immediately changed her training from high volume to low volume. Each session would only last forty-five minutes max. As the session was shorter in length this allowed for greater intensity within the session. Previously there were four classes per week, plus two or three home practices, so I reduced it down to only three sessions per week. The total volume was only three forty-five minute sessions per week, scheduled for Monday, Wednesday and Friday. That was all she was allowed.

Having been used to such a high volume of work, the dancer and teacher immediately seemed worried given I had asked her not to dance for four weeks and then limited her to only three short sessions per week, but given their approach had not worked for the last few years they had nothing to lose and agreed to go with it.

Training information

The three sessions worked on developing the dancer's speed, strength and structural balance. One day per week we would spend the whole session working on opposing muscle groups *(muscle groups that are not used much in class)*. The second day we would work on speed / lactic acid based sprint work on an athletics track, and the third day consisted of basic strength work such as weighted squats, step ups, etc. in a gym-based environment. Her four rest days per week consisted of some light mobility and flexibility work to aid the recovery process.

Results

After four weeks when we sat down and looked at her training logs we could see marked improvements in her strength, speed and structural balance. The dancer's ability to tolerate lactic acid was also greater.

After the four week period I allowed the dancer to resume attendance at dance class and we immediately saw a significant improvement in her dance performance even though she hadn't danced for four weeks. Teacher, dancer and even parents were astounded by how much progress had been made is such a short space of time. The answer was simple.

How?

As the dancer had done the same training year round for the last several years, the training stimulus was no longer new to the body therefore the body did not need to progress anymore as it was no longer a shock. Simply by taking the athlete away from the training she had grown so accustomed to and placing her into a new environment incorporating different exercises and speeds, while enforcing less volume and less duration in her training it completely changed the training stimulus and as a result her body was shocked and forced to adapt to it. This led to a rise in her performance.

This study shows the importance of changing our training, changing the type of training we do and breaking this down into different phases throughout the year to avoid plateaus, overworking muscle groups and injuries. The girl went back into her dancing schedule and trained three times a week at dance class and continued to complete two strength and speed sessions each week for the remainder of the year. She later went on to achieve her highest placing ever by a large margin.

To be clear, I'm not suggesting we should all stop dancing for four weeks, this is not necessary. And as this study was only conducted with one athlete I cannot say for a fact that it would work for everyone – success depends on many factors. However, the main take home points are there for everyone. If you incorporate certain aspects of this into your own training schedules and take away from the study the fact that variability in training is such an important factor for an athlete's progression it would certainly help improve performance for most dancers, especially those who have stopped making progress. Always remember **changes must be made on a regular basis to ensure the dancer keeps progressing.**

The use of different types of training to improve Irish dance performance

If we are totally honest dancers are always going to be quite limited when it comes to variability in class training given the lack of space and lack of equipment a confined studio can offer. We need to think outside the box.

Dancing is a sport that never takes advantage of the benefits external training can bring. Given the correct type of training is chosen, other sports and different types of training can be a great boost to an Irish dancer's performance.

We very rarely see instances of dancers completing any sprint work on track or finding a local park and completing some hill conditioning sessions. There are also very few dancers who will complete any structural balance or structured strength work in the gym. All of their training is centred around what goes on inside a dance studio, which is fine; however, when we are looking for ways to change our training programmes frequently, we need some options to change to.

Most other sports will have their athletes use other types of training to benefit their main sports performance. A 100 metre sprinter will not train for his event by running 100 metres every session. He will include regular strength work and plyometric training outside of the regular track sessions.

His training on the track would also be changed as the season approached. For example, if his main event is 100 metres, very rarely would he go out and run 100 metres as part of his training session. He would train over 200-400 metres in the off season for endurance and over 20-60 metres in season for raw speed, then click it all together pre-competition to have all the fundamental components that make a great sprinter.

Similar to that example, a boxer does not box twelve rounds every day at training, but rather will work on different elements of his sport at different times of the year and then put it all together to ensure that they peak at the right time. A boxer's preparation will include hill sprints for conditioning work, strength work in the gym and track work for raw speed. All these things are completed far away from the ring.

Regardless of the exact details of an athlete's training it is important that we see the great variance that each sport has in their training programmes. As long as the external training is kept within the requirements of the primary sport this variety of training allows for constant changes of programming, creating new overloading parameters and avoiding training plateaus.

How would we include external training into a dancer's programme?

Let's take for example a dancer completing five classes per week. We would say she is at the high end of frequency and there is not much more she can add in, right? A general rule is that to add in a session we must take something away. Firstly, let's say we strip this dancer's training days back down to three days per week. This now frees up another two days and keeps two days for recovery.

Now, as a dancer requires great speed, speed endurance and the ability to tolerate high volumes of lactic acid, it would be a great option to include a session that would improve all of these key areas.

We could start by including one weekly hill sprint in the off season for lactic acid based training and track sprints during the in season, focusing on acceleration. That way we are covering the main fundamentals of what makes a great Irish dancer without even being in a dance hall. This brings the dancer back up to four days' training, but still only three dancing.

Now, as Irish dancing is a multidirectional sport it is a high priority to be structurally balanced. Therefore we could also include one day per week of strength training in a gym-based environment, focusing on balance and stability (or home-based medicine ball work for the younger dancer). This again is completed away from the studio; however, it is working on the dancer's ability to get stronger and stabilise that newly developed strength.

This provides the fifth day of training and brings the dancer back to training the same number of times per week as before; however, two of those days are focusing on a completely different training stimulus.

The main benefit of changing the two days is the improvement of speed, lactic acid tolerance, structural balance and strength in her performance. However, as this dancer is away from class more she has new motivation from being in a different environment, which also means when back in class the dancer will get much more out of her dancing practice as she's reduced the volume from five to three sessions.

I recommend as a school or group of dancers that you all get together and plan weekly local group sessions at a steep hill or track. Keep the school together, race each other, feed off each other, boost morale, and ultimately everyone will get better in the process. You can even get the parents to join in, suddenly they will no longer want to stay and watch!

Training phases for Irish dancing – off season, pre-season and in season

We have covered the benefits of changing programmes regularly; however, collectively – as a sport – we need to find a common structure that we can all operate from.

The one area that every sport has in common is the separation of off season and in season training. I have yet to come across any competitive sport in the world that does not break their year down into off season and in season blocks, with the exception of competitive Irish dance. Therefore I recommend this to be a good base to start from, and recommend we break our training phases down together.

Some sports have longer off seasons than others. Take, for example, soccer: they only have a handful of weeks each year in which to fit in some off season training. Compare that to a track athlete who will compete only in summer, and has the whole winter as off season.

There are many major fundamental reasons why coaches include off season and in season training into their athlete's programme and as dancers or teachers if we are also going to do this we will need to understand the benefits of doing so. I have listed a few below:

1. Injury prevention
2. Long-term performance
3. Goal setting
4. Mindset / motivation
5. Peaking at the right time

1. Injury prevention

When we are dancing we recruit certain muscle groups to do what we need to do. For example, quadriceps and calves are primary movers in Irish dance. Now, if we train the same way all year round, this means that we are asking the same muscles to work year round with no consideration to the opposing muscle groups that are underused in dancing. This is a fundamental reason why Irish dancing has such a high injury rate.

We spend all year training our quadriceps so that eventually they generate too much power for what our hamstrings can safely tolerate, resulting in injury. When was the last time you actually spent six weeks strengthening your hamstrings instead of stretching them?

One massive reason to incorporate off season training into your schedule is so that you can spend that time strengthening the opposing muscle groups that aren't used during the year. This is how we achieve structural balance.

2. Long-term performance

The alteration through different training phases from off season into in season will use different energy systems at different intensities. This alteration gives the body a break from the training type that came before it and the training that will come next. It will help to avoid overtraining and burnout from too much repetition, and also look after your long-term health and performance, meaning you can continue your sport for many years having conditioned yourself properly.

3. Goal setting

Having different training phases means there is a start date and an end date to each phase. Having a timeframe means we can now attach small goals to be achieved by the end of each phase.

Put simply, setting goals makes the dancer's performance measurable each year. *(More on measurable performance later.)* It also allows the dancer to look back at what their training results were at the same time last year and aim to improve on it. Without goals and targets we are simply hoping to get there by chance.

4. Mindset / motivation

Structuring different seasons throughout the year allows the athlete to avoid becoming demotivated. These changes keep their focus on training and don't allow the dancer to get distracted from the sport by becoming bored and lethargic due to always completing the same training.

5. Peaking at the right time

The structure allows for gradual continued improvements in performance right up to the day of competition. This allows a dancer to reach their potential at exactly the right time, also known as 'peaking'. Peaking allows a dancer to be on top performance for the most important competition(s) of the year.

Now that we have spoken about the importance of us all breaking down our year into different phases, how do we actually structure this for class? And what aspects of the training changes in each phase?

There is no one rule that states this is exactly how the year must be structured or laid out; there are many different methods of yearly programming that would produce the same results. However, let's start with a basic layout.

I have given you an overview of how I have arranged many dancers' training phases in the past. I have found this method to work extremely well and it's produced some great results as-well as undoubtedly having prevented many injuries.

Let's start by dividing the dancing year into four phases

1. Off season
2. Pre-season
3. In season
4. Maintenance *(if required)*

Off season

Goals for the off season would be focused around developing a base level of conditioning, what will be known to most of you as stamina or speed endurance. We would also look to establish a solid foundation focusing on muscle imbalances, structural balance and strengthening opposing muscle groups that will not get much work the rest of the year, thus reducing the chances of injury. The off season phase is best to develop a good solid foundation from which we can add speed and strength in the next phases. Off season training is often the most skipped phase of training, simply because it tends to be the toughest and furthest away from competition, so motivation is lacking. Those that skip the off season will usually find it quite hard to develop any real speed, power or sharpness come the in season. The saying, **'You cannot fire a canon from a canoe'** couldn't be more true when it comes to an Irish dancer. In order for us to develop great strength, speed and power we must first develop a solid foundation that can stabilise that power and speed. Without this your body simply will not allow you to get too strong or fast because you will have an inability to stabilise a greater output of speed and power safely, resulting in injury.

What happens if you go too fast down a hill on a skateboard? Eventually the speed will become too much to stabilise and you will fall off, right? Now, imagine I could make your major muscles produce enough force for you to jump three metres high, but I never allowed you to strengthen the minor, smaller muscles responsible for stabilising you upon landing. What do you think would happen? It's almost certainly going to cause an injury, right?

The body is extremely smart and will hold back on how fast you get or how strong you become, depending on how much force you can safely stabilise. In my opinion this is why off season training is the most important of all the phases. Build your foundation working from the ground up and not only should you have an injury free year, but your performance will improve as a result of the base work, the benefits of which will stay with you throughout the year.

To develop a base line of fitness we would aim to include one day per week of endurance training, such as hill sprints or interval based running, with each run lasting two to three minutes in duration with equal or less recovery time. Two to three minutes may not seem like much endurance; however, two to three minutes is endurance work for a forty-five to sixty second event.

For structural balance training we would look to include one session per week of strength work devoted entirely to strengthening the opposing muscle groups, such as upper back, lower back, glutes and hamstrings.

Pre-season

At this stage the dancer should be well conditioned and have built a solid foundation. It's now time to move to the next phase. The aim of pre-season training for a dancer should be to develop their strength and improve lactic acid tolerance. Whereas the last phase was aimed more at speed, endurance and stamina, we are now looking to add speed and strength to the new foundation in the pre-season phase.

To do this we would aim to complete strength training once per week for the older dancers, focusing on major strength lifts such as squats, split squats, and step ups that will improve dance performance. For younger dancers I have included a full section discussing suitable training later in this chapter.

Lactic acid production is the aim in the running session. We would look to include sprints lasting around forty to sixty seconds, as not only will this mimic stage time, but each run will put a dancer firmly in the lactic acid zone, improving their ability to tolerate it much more effectively.

In season

From the off season and pre-season phases we have now developed a solid foundation and added strength to that foundation. We should now both have the ability to finish dances strongly and a much improved lactic acid tolerance level. However, a stronger muscle does not necessary mean a faster muscle.

Now that we are into the in season training phase we will be close to major competitions. As all the endurance and strength work has been completed in the previous phases, the aim of in season training for a dancer should be to focus on raw speed over a short distance. Key areas such as aggression, power, reaction time and acceleration over a short distance are important here to mimic top speed across a short dance stage. The hard work has been done in the previous phases; the aim now is to piece everything together, sharpening up all the steps and firing up those fast twitch muscle fibres.

To improve all these fundamental areas it would be wise at this point to shorten the duration of lactic acid sprints from the last phase of forty to sixty seconds and bring them right down to twenty to sixty metre sprints, or around nought to fifteen seconds per run for pure speed work. This will work on the dancer's power, speed, acceleration and reaction time without creating too much fatigue in each session. This sets the dancer up nicely for improved recovery and moves into the peak period pre-competition.

Any strength training being completed must now be changed to focus on high force ballistic movements, such as plyometrics, agility training and cone drills. Everything we do from this point on must be explosive, powerful and sharp, with minimum volume and maximum intensity.

Many dancers struggle to achieve maximal speed and sharpness. This is unfortunately due to completing so much endurance training that their brain tends to organise muscle contractions in the same manner – slow and cyclical movements repeated over and over. Just look at a marathon runner and how robotic-like they appear when they run, as their brain organises the same contractions and movements time and time again.

The problem with dancers trying to improve their power and sharpness is that if we have been training the muscles to contract in a slow, robotic form by completing lots of aerobic work, it is extremely hard for the brain to suddenly switch and produce high force ballistic movements when the muscle is not trained in that manner. To enable a dancer to be sharp we must train in a manner that requires high force ballistic movements in all directions, involving acceleration, deceleration and lift off the ground. This is why it is so important to include this phase of training in the build-up to a competition.

Maintenance

The aim of a maintenance phase is to maintain the optimal performance levels that you have built up over previous phases across a given time frame. This phase would be placed between two or more important competitions that are scheduled together across a short period. As a gap of a few weeks between competitions wouldn't allow for another full cycle of the above off / pre / in season phases, we would then slot in a maintenance phase to maintain top performance from one competition to the next. As you can imagine, the longer you try to peak for, the less effective it will be, given that optimal performance can only be maintained for a limited period of time. That time period is of no set length and will vary between athlete and sport; however, most athletes will learn their own optimal performance time through experience when it comes to maintaining performance for a given length of time.

I have provided you with a table summary below of all the above training information and its relevance in each section. I have also provided you with sample competition calendars to show how to effectively plan each phase in the year. The tables highlight the most important competition of the year and then schedule all the phases around this. We also look at an example of where to include a maintenance phase. As a teacher or coach you can use this template and create your own yearly training plan for your dancers, centred around their main goal for the coming year.

These are just brief examples to show the meaning behind the text you have just read. Please remember all of the training programmes and explanations of everything discussed is at the back of the book. There are sections on applying endurance training, lactic acid training, plyometrics, agility, cone drills and more. Please refer to the back when putting this all into practice.

Overview of a yearly training structure for Irish dancing

Training Goal	Off Season	Pre-Season	In Season	Maintenance
Anaerobic Session	Endurance – up to 3 minutes	Speed endurance / lactic acid zone – 40-60 seconds	Raw speed – 0-15 seconds	Mix between speed endurance & speed
Strength Session	Structural balance / opposing muscle groups	Strength – working on all major strength lifts	Power – focusing on moving the load, fast, sharp and powerful	Mix between strength & power
Dance Class Session: Steps	Learning new steps / breaking down steps	Analysing different sections of the dance, correcting technique & errors	Polishing technique	Mix between pre-season & in season work

Dances	Dancing full dances with minimal recovery (1-2 minutes)	Dancing full dances to failure (3-5 minutes recovery)	3-4 full dances max with ample recovery time to allow heart rate to return to normal. (5-10 minutes)	(Depending on length of time separating competitions. If only a matter of days / a week, strictly in season work only. If 4-8 weeks pre-season, then in season combined.)
Interval based dance work	Endurance Drill work to failure (1-2 minute drills with equal or less recovery)	Lactic acid based drill work to failure (60 second drills with 2 minute recovery)	Speed drills – short & sharp, avoiding failure (15-30 second drills with 2-3 minutes recovery)	

Yearly calendar

You may have noticed that I haven't given a specific duration for each phase. So how long does each last? There is no clear answer here, it will depend totally on the dancer's competition schedule. However, it is important to note that it is possible to complete more than one set of off season, pre-season and in season cycles in a year. Many sports will have two off seasons in a year. I have had dancers complete two full cycles of the above in order to have them peak twice in one year.

Alternatively there may be a time where there are two important competitions quite close together, maybe only a month or two apart. As there would not be sufficient time to go through a full cycle again, at this point we would add in a maintenance phase to maintain performance and peak across both competitions. As you see it's entirely dependent on the competition calendar and it is something that the dance teacher, strength coach and dancer must sit down and plan for at the beginning of each year.

I have provided you with some yearly schedule examples below:

Dancer peaking for 1 major competition per year
(non-world qualifiers)

Month	Competition	Training Phase	Duration
January		Off Season	
February		Off Season	16 week Off Season
March		Off Season	
April		Off Season	
May		Pre-Season	
June		Pre-Season	12 Week Pre-Season
July		Pre-Season	
August		In Season	
September		In Season	12 Week In Season
October		In Season	
November	Oireachtas	Peak	Peak
December		REST	2-4 weeks

Table 1 overview

The above yearly planner shows how a dancer and teacher might plan their training schedule for the year ahead.

The dancer in this example would only have one major competition in the year, therefore all training seasons must be planned with the aim of having the athlete peak at the right time. In this scenario the main goal for the year is to have the dancer in the best shape possible and injury free by the Oireachtas in November. All smaller competitions are planned around this. The training phases must always be planned around the most important event of the year, as shown.

Dancer peaking for 2 competitions per year *(world qualifiers)*

Month	Competition	Training Phase	Duration
January		Off Season	4 week – Pre-Season 1
February		Pre-Season	4 week – Pre-Season 1
March		In Season	4 week – In Season 2
April	**World Championships**	**Peak**	**Peak**
May		Off Season	8 Week – Off Season 2
June		Off Season	
July		Pre-Season	8 Week – Pre-Season 2
August		Pre-Season	
September		In Season	8 Week – In Season
October		In Season	
November	**Oireachtas**	**Competition Peaking**	**Peak**
December		REST	2-4 weeks

Table 2 overview

This schedule shows how to plan a schedule for when there is more than one important event in a dancer's yearly calendar.

For most, you are going to have to qualify for the World Championships, which is the main goal of the year. However, if the dancer successfully qualifies for the worlds we then have another major competition to plan into the training schedule. As shown in this example, after qualifying at the Oireachtas there would be four full months between competitions. It is not realistic for the dancer to maintain peak performance *(especially through the Christmas period)* until the World Championships. In my experience the dancer would more than likely become fatigued and performance would have dropped by that stage. Instead, after a short rest post qualifying, we have sufficient time to go through a short four week off / pre / in season set of training phases to ensure the dancer can get to the world stage injury free and peaking at their best again.

Dancer peaking for 3 competitions close together

(with maintenance phase)

Month	Competition	Training Phase	Duration
January		Off Season	4 weeks
February		Pre-Season	4 weeks
March		In Season	4 weeks
April	**World Championships**	**Peak**	**Peak**
May		Maintenance	8 Weeks
June		Maintenance	
July	**Nationals**	**Peak**	**Peak**
August		Off Season	4 weeks
September		Pre-Season	4 weeks
October		In Season	4 weeks
November	**Oireachtas**	**Peak**	**Peak**
December		REST	4 weeks

Table 3 overview

The final example shows how we would plan for three majors per year, with two of those competitions being relatively close together.

This scenario has the dancer wanting to be close to optimal performance for the World Championships, then the American National Championships, and then later for the Oireachtas. In this instance we would need to have the dancer close to peak performance for April and then add in a maintenance phase throughout May and June, until the nationals. As the competitions will only be around eight to ten weeks apart it should be possible to maintain peak performance for this given timeframe without increasing the risk of injury or burnout, as long as a long rest period is given at the end of the year, as shown in the December slot

I have used all three schedules above with great success for both beginner, intermediate and advanced level dancers.

As a teacher, you'll find yearly planning will work really well for compliant dancers who work well with structure. It gives them a roadmap to success for the year and knowing they can see the path that will take them to the biggest competition of the year in peak condition improves the dancer's confidence.

We must factor in that not every dancer's performance will

progress at the same rate, and whilst it's great to have a plan at the start of the year, sometimes changes have to be made mid-season for a variety of reasons. There will be dancers who make slower progress for reasons such as illness, injury, study commitments, holidays, school, or simply because they are less compliant and dedicated than the others within the group.

For this situation changes need to be made, and the best rule to remember for any teacher or coach responsible for the yearly programming of dancers is to firstly programme for the group and later adjust for the individual when required.

Programme for the group, adjust for the individual

We know that giving the same programme to a group of athletes will generate small success for those in individualised sports. There are, however, some major fundamentals that we can blanket cover as a starting point for the group and then as we progress we can adjust small aspects according to how each dancer responds. Programming for the group is a fantastic tool to get things off the mark, but after that it's important that we tailor for the individual by checking and recording the progress of each dancer.

So how do we check for progression? We need to measure performance!

Measuring performance – fitness testing for competitive Irish dance

Dancing is a non-measurable sport – meaning there are no proper measurement tools in place for a dancer to compare their progress against. On top of that the competition results are in the hands of a panel of judges, meaning it is possible that these results can also be skewed slightly given we are relying on a human marking system to determine how well we do compared to the more accurate computerised marking systems we see in other sports.

In class we simply have to rely on feedback from our teachers to know if we are dancing well or not. Even if your teacher thinks you are dancing well, is this compared to the rest of your class? Or you country, or all the dancers in world? There is nothing to compare our performance against other than those around us. Many dancers go into competition feeling they are dancing really well, based on how they dance in class in comparison to the standard of the other dancers. However, once that dancer gets out on stage, they are being compared to the best dancers in the world. All of a sudden what they were measuring performance by on a weekly basis is irrelevant, and it often results in disappointment.

Every other sport has measurement tools in place to ensure athletes are on track and more importantly so that they know the training they are completing each week is working. As a sprinter you have your times on the track each week to measure performance, similar to athletes who complete strength work in the gym who will have their strength records to show them exactly how they are progressing. As a dancer very little of what we currently do is measurable in class, but what about outside class?

There are many ways in which a dancer can incorporate measurement tools into their training. This will provide both dancer and teacher with factual information relating to the dancer's current ability level and from this changes can be made to ensure continued progression.

How do we measure dance performance without actually dancing?

We know that the dancing itself cannot be measured (unless we analyse the biomechanics of the dancer through computerised software). However, we can look at what key attributes make a great dancer and then measure those areas individually. We have already covered what all these performance areas are – speed, power, strength, flexibility, mobility and speed endurance / lactic acid tolerance and structural balance – we now just need to know the relevant tests to apply to each area.

Fitness testing gives dancers a platform from which to measure their performance each week and holds each person accountable through each phase of the year. If a dancer can see they are getting faster, sharper and stronger this is almost always reflected in their dance performance and motivation levels, not to mention that their confidence will grow.

If a dancer isn't showing improvements in the tests, that is when I apply the **programme for the group – adjust for the individual** rule and start to change small aspects of the training to better suit the individual's requirements. It is not a bad thing to have tested performance and identified little or no improvement. The key is that the test picks this up early enough to allow the dance teacher sufficient time to change the training programme and leaves sufficient time to get progress going.

Without testing there would be no way of knowing whether the training was working or not and you then risk a full season of poor performances. Remember, even though training can feel difficult it does not mean it is improving performance. This is why I recommend that all dancers and teachers implement regular testing for their school.

Below I have listed a few different basic testing methods that I have used in the past and currently use for dancers I work with. The options listed are the most successful and easiest for you all to implement into your school.

I have listed nine tests in total. You can quite easily implement the first seven tests into your training immediately. They require no equipment and can be done both in class and on an outdoor track surface. The last two tests listed are advanced tests and must be carried out by a qualified practitioner.

The aim would be to test all of the dancers in each relevant area, depending upon which part of the season they are in.

Basic tests:
Bleep test
400 m lactic acid test
60 m / 100 m sprint test
Flexibility tests
Core tests
Vertical jump
Standing long jump

Advanced tests – *(practitioner required)*:
Structural balance testing
Maximal strength testing

Bleep test *(overall fitness)*

The bleep test is a measure of an athlete's VO_2 max and lung capacity *(maximal oxygen uptake)*. It is usually completed over a 20 metre *(or 15 metre)* distance and is completed in a shuttle run format – back and forth. The test is progressive in that you will pace your speed to the time of a beep. As the beep gets quicker, you too must speed up to ensure you reach the shuttle mark before the beep sounds. Eventually the beep will outrun you and this failure level will mark your max effort and your result for the test.

As this test is a measure of your aerobic endurance, I recommend placing it in the off season phase where endurance and stamina are the priorities. Testing is recommended at the start of the off season training phase to show starting fitness levels and at the end of the off season training phase to show progress made in the target areas.

I would also recommend testing any new or beginner dancers to the class as a basic fitness entry level assessment.

This test is currently available as an app on all android phones and is very easily accessed to be used in class.

Equipment needed:
Bleep test app and speakers usable on your phone / laptop

400 m test *(lactic acid / speed endurance)*

Everyone knows that 400 metres is seen as arguably the hardest discipline, given its toughness. This is due to the massively high lactate production in the event. Not only is it a sprint, but it is also a measure of how long you can maintain that speed. The distance is usually run around forty-five to sixty seconds at a high standard, and therefore its time duration puts the event firmly in the lactic acid zone. As Irish dancers perform around the same timeframe they require a high tolerance to lactic acid. The test is simple. After a thorough warm up have each dancer run 400 metres as fast as they can and record their time. This is a perfect way to test a dancer for both their lactic acid tolerance and their speed endurance.

I recommend this test be carried out at the start of the pre-season training phase, when lactic acid training is a priority to show the athlete's current anaerobic lactic acid threshold and at the end of the pre-season training phase to show progress made in this area.

Equipment needed:
Marked 400 metre athletics track
Stopwatch

60 m / 100 m test *(speed / acceleration)*

The 60 metre test is a measure of raw speed, power and acceleration across a short distance. It will measure the ability of the dancer's fast twitch fibres, given the quick reaction and drive phase required in the sprint. This test is recommended for in season training as it is perfectly placed several weeks out from competition, where the aim is to develop the short-term power, speed and acceleration capabilities of the dancer to replicate stage distance and sharpness.

If the athlete is poor at sprinting and cannot turn on their fast twitch muscle fibres effectively they will have a difficult time getting up to top speed over the first 30-60 metres, so will probably find the test very easy. Imagine getting a marathon runner to sprint 60 metres, they will produce very little speed and power and the test will be quite easy and ineffective.

In that case I would recommend extending the distance up to 100 metres to allow for greater acceleration room to get up to full speed. Of course you would aim to reduce the distance of the test once the athlete develops more of a fast twitch ability to generate sufficient power and get to full speed over a relatively short distance.

As dancers we have a 20-30 metre distance on a stage so it is of great importance to teach a dancer how to get to full power and speed over as little distance as possible, otherwise the first section of the dance will be quite slow in nature, allowing the dancer to slowly build up the speed and momentum. This needs to be avoided.

I recommend this test be carried out at the start of the in season training phase and again at the end of the in season training phase, right before competition, to show progress made in the target areas.

Equipment needed:
Marked 100 metre athletics track
Stopwatch

Flexibility / mobility tests

Your current level of flexibility is defined as the range of motion available without strain or pull against other muscle attachments. Whilst there is no single test to assess the flexibility of the body as a whole, we must test the flexibility of individual areas to create a full picture. When we are measuring flexibility we are looking for the actual degrees of distance available to the muscle and joint. Once taken, compare this to the amount of flexibility that muscle or joint requires for athletic performance to see if improvements need to be made. With dancers generally using the same muscle groups year round we tend to find limited range of motion in the hip and ankle joints, and limited flexibility in the hip flexors, quads and calves.

To test the limit of someone's current range of motion, you need to ensure the body is not disrupted whilst the test is being completed. Once the body position is affected we know we have gone beyond the athlete's current available range of motion.

For example, a simple hamstring test would be to lie flat on the ground and have someone raise one leg slowly. At some point you will reach your limit and you will see the opposite knee raise slightly. This is what we call the strain of the other muscle attachments and once we see other parts of the body beginning to pull or move, we know the limit has been reached. From there we can measure or judge the distance from the heel of the raised leg to the floor. This distance can be measured in degrees or inches / centimetres.

I recommend flexibility testing be done on a yearly basis. A stronger muscle is generally a tighter muscle, therefore as the athlete gets stronger and faster they will also get tighter. Regular testing will ensure we maintain the required level of flexibility and mobility. *(More on this in chapter 5.)*

I would also recommend flexibility testing for any new or beginner dancers to the class as a basic entry assessment.

Equipment needed:
Tape measure
Camera for visual markers

Core tests

The aim of core testing is to measure the current level of strength the athlete has in their abdominal and lower back muscles. The tests can be quite simple in nature for the beginner athlete. Something such as a basic plank will test the dancer on the strength endurance level of the core muscles, given they are engaging them properly.

The problem with a plank test is the dancer can simply rest on their elbows and toes with little core engagement. To make this a fair test we must ensure they are maximally contracting the target muscles for the duration of the test.

For the more advanced dancer we can increase the difficulty of the test by forcing some instability in the body, making the core muscles engage harder. A three point plank, removing one limb at a time (leg/arm) and forcing the body to stabilise on three contact points instead of the regular four, is an easy way to increase the difficulty of the test.

To test the strength of the abdominals and lower back muscles we can get the athlete to lie flat on the floor and raise their legs to a ninety degree angle. Place your fingers underneath the athlete's lower back and get them to slowly lower both legs. At some point, as the legs near the floor, the lower back will raise up. This raise indicates a weakness in that area. Record the distance the legs are from the floor at the point when the lower back pulled away from your fingers. The aim is to be able to keep the lower back flat throughout the whole movement until the heels touch the floor.

Whilst core testing can be done at any stage of the year, ideally we would want to know the strength of the core as soon as possible. It is responsible for stabilisation of the pelvis as-well as posture and carriage support, so we can potentially protect the athlete from many injuries if we test early in the season then programme to fix any issues.

I would also recommend testing the core strength of any new or beginner athletes to the class as an entry level assessment.

Equipment needed:
Yoga mat / soft surface mat

The vertical jump *(lower body power output)*

The vertical jump is a test designed to measure the power output and elastic strength of the dancer's lower body. This is a perfect test for dancers as the sport involves a take-off and landing element in training and competition.

The test requires the dancer to chalk their fingers and stand side on against a wall. The dancer will squat, then produce as much jumping force as possible in one upward motion. At the highest peak of the jump the dancer will touch the wall with his / her arm fully extended and mark the height achieved via the chalk on their fingers. The teacher will then have a tape measure at hand to measure the distance of the mark from the floor.

The vertical jump test is important throughout the year; however, I would recommend implementing this test at the beginning and end of the in season phase, where the priority is power and explosive strength. It is also a great test to implement for any dancers going through a fat loss phase, as their power to weight ratio will improve as body fat reduces. This will have a great impact on how high the dancer can jump simply because the load is now lighter helping to motivate the dancer to reach their ideal competition weight.

Equipment needed:
Tape measure
Chalk
Wall (that can be marked)

The standing long jump *(lower body power output)*

This test requires the dancer to perform a two-legged jump from a static position across a maximal distance. The dancer will squat, then produce as much jumping force as possible, aiming for maximal upward and forward momentum. When they land, the teacher will use a tape measure to measure the distance from the starting point to the landing mark left by the heel *(the closest body part to the start)*. The standing long jump is best completed on an easily measurable surface, such as a long jump pit / sand pit.

I would recommend implementing this test at the beginning and end of the in season phase, where the priority is power and explosive strength. Just like the vertical jump, it is another great test to implement for a dancer going through a fat loss phase as their power to weight ratio will improve as their body fat reduces, which will have a great impact on how far the dancer can propel themselves simply because the load being moved is now lighter. This will help to motivate the dancer to reach ideal competition weight and highlight the importance of staying lean for optimal performance.

Equipment needed:
Sand pit / long jump pit
Tape measure

Advanced testing – by a qualified practitioner only

My aim is not to teach you how to complete the following tests. It is to make you all aware that advanced testing options are available, explain how they may benefit you, and point you in the direction of a practitioner who can conduct these at your request. For this reason I have not noted the required equipment as this would be supplied by the practitioner / coach.

Structural balance testing

Structural balance testing is required for athletes in multi-directional sports, as given the multiple angles and directions of force the athlete requires structural balance in all areas. The body will naturally be stronger in the muscles that are more frequently used and less strength will be found in the underdeveloped muscle groups. Structural balance testing is an advanced testing method and should be carried out by a qualified strength practitioner trained in assessing athletes in structural balance.

An example of one structural balance test would be the Klatt test. The Klatt test has the athlete stand on one leg on a low platform. The athlete then hops off the platform, landing about three or four inches in front of it, and aims to stabilise the landing on one foot. The assessor will look at what happens upon impact of the foot on the floor, which will then identify weaknesses and imbalances in the lower body.

For example, if the knee falls inward upon landing, that identifies potential weakness in the knee. Another indicator would be if the dancer lands on one foot then has to take several hops in one direction before being able to finally stabilise the landing, identifying further imbalances that are pulling on one side of the body.

The primary purpose of the Klatt test is to determine any weaknesses in the knee, hips, glutes pelvis and lower back.

This test, however, is only one example of many different tests that come in a structural balance assessment. There are many different methods of testing for structural balance in the upper and lower body that can be carried out by a qualified practitioner if necessary.

I would recommend any serious dancer at a high level undergo a structural balance test once per year, at the beginning of the off season. For most this may not be possible or necessary; however, where it would be of great value is in those who are already at a high level, or when seeking to find the cause of repeating injuries. Repetitive injuries can occur due to muscle imbalances and structural balance testing can help to identify where the weakness is. The practitioner can then put together a plan to eliminate any weakness or imbalance identified during the testing.

Maximal strength testing

Maximal strength testing is used to find out a dancer's peak strength for a single repetition.

The exercises chosen can be generic or sport-specific type exercises that replicate movement patterns used in dancing. For competitive Irish dancers I have used the following two exercises successfully to determine strength levels.

Barbell squat

The aim of the test is to assess the current lower body strength of a dancer. The barbell squat is a good predictor of a dancer's vertical jump height and lift off the ground, and can be used with dancers who have training experience in gym and strength work.

Pull up

The aim of this test is to assess the current upper body strength of a dancer. The pull up will indicate their upper back strength, which we now know is needed for posture, structural balance and to counteract the power of the legs to avoid rotation and twisting. *(More on this in chapter 5.)*

Some parents may express concern over implementing one rep max testing for athletes due to the high load being used. If the athlete has no previous experience in handling heavy loads these tests would not be used. If the athlete has little experience in strength training we can use three or five repetition max strength tests, so that the load can be reduced across the higher reps, and keep one rep max testing for the advanced athlete.

Strength training for the younger dancer (under 16 years old)

Children training with weights has long been a topic for discussion between parents, coaches and sports clubs.

As over half of competitive Irish dancers are below the age of sixteen, I feel it is massively important to discuss these issues and leave you all with a clear understanding of the potential benefits and any risks associated with strength training for the younger athlete.

The theory is that any type of strength training under the age of sixteen can be detrimental to bone growth. We also quite commonly hear that weight training is bad for our joints.

So where did these theories come from, and is there evidence to support these claims?

To date there has been no research to show that weight training will stunt bone growth in any human at any age. There is also no evidence to prove that weight training is detrimental to our joint health, given proper exercise technique and load is applied. Further to this, recent studies show that growth plates are not affected – either positively or negatively – by a wide range of sports and training modalities. [7 , 9]

Just as it is human nature to protect our children, it is our automatic reaction to think that something heavy surely can't be good for them. We want to believe that we are protecting children from injury and allowing them to grow. In my past seminars, even after I have explained that there is no research to support the above claims, I still find that people simply don't want to believe or don't trust it.

In reality there is much more chance of injury occurring by allowing our children to play sports such as rugby or football and, of course, dancing. These sports, due to their impactive nature, have a high injury rate. There is also biomechanics research that supports things like running, throwing, jumping, and hitting produce larger forces on the body than strength training does. [5]

If we focus on just the dancer for a second, dancers produce a tremendous amount of force through their ankle, shin and knee joints upon take-off and landing on every step. This constant impact is far worse than any force that would be going through their joints when completing weight training, where their feet are firmly on the ground.

In fact, research shows that strength training can reduce the risk of injury in several ways. The enhanced muscular strength increases joint stability, which serves to dissipate high levels of joint force during explosive sprints, jumps, landings and high agility movements.[12] This is perfect news for dancers of all ages.

Given Irish dancing is a high impact sport this could be another reason why so many dancers could potentially be getting injured as very little strength training is being completed to counteract or stabilise the joints.

For any parent that is concerned about strength training for their children I ask you to pick up their school bag the next time you're driving them to school, or simply observe a group of school kids walking to school. You will notice the sheer weight in the bags they carry and also how they tend to lean to one side and force their posture out of the natural position. This in its own right is a load bearing task and is essentially weight training. Carrying a heavy bag on your back for a short or long duration is no different than placing a barbell on your back.

Another important factor to look at is something as simple as a child playing in a park or on a tree. Kids will jump off certain obstacles from high heights almost daily when growing up. The amount of force going through their body upon landing is much greater than any force produced by strength training.

For anyone with great concerns over their children completing strenuous exercise, would you go so far as to not allow them to carry a school bag or play in a park? Given most of the readers of this book will have allowed their children to complete dance class training several times a week, then most of you have already allowed these forces to travel through your child's joints and ultimately you have greatly increased the risk of your child's injury potential.

Whatever we do at any age, there will be a certain risk attached to it. Whilst it is not essential for children to complete strength training, it would certainly be beneficial for many. It will help create a solid foundation and a base that is strong enough to support both daily tasks, such as carrying schoolbags, and also ensure they are structurally balanced enough to avoid injury risk in dance class.

A high percentage of dancers finish their dance career still quite young, meaning most will never realise their full potential. Given most will only begin strength training late in their career they have missed the most important part of development for the younger athlete.

It is well known that Eastern European coaches were some of the first to have their children completing strength and flexibility training from the ages of five or six. Some lessons can be learnt *from* a region that produces world class teenage athletes every year on the benefits of strength training for the younger athlete.

Training rules for the younger athlete

We know that strength training for anyone is beneficial, given it is completed correctly. However, there are a few rules that I would implement to ensure the training is completed correctly and at the low intensities they require.

1. Bodyweight training does not have to come first

Exercises such as bodyweight squats, bodyweight step ups, and bodyweight lunges will all prove difficult in the beginning without having to add any extra weight, and may be a good starting point for many. However, the reverse can also be true. If we look at bodyweight exercises such as pull ups, these require the dancer to have a great deal of initial strength to complete.

The dancer may not be strong enough to complete a full pull up; however, we could have them complete a pull down on a resistance machine with a much lighter load than their body weight, which would reduce the intensity of the exercise. When the dancer then increases their strength, we may see pull ups being added in later in the programming after resistance training has been completed for a period of time.

2. Use moderate loads

Like anything, as the teenager will be new to strength training they will get greater improvements faster and with lighter weights than an adult would. Therefore any loads used must be moderate and within their current strength capabilities. When adding additional weight to the exercise we can start with light dumbbell or resistance band work. Dumbbells and resistance bands allow for free movement of the arms and allow the athlete to drop them at any time.

3. Apply the ten per cent rule

When increasing the weight, adopt the ten per cent rule. This rule inhibits you from increasing the weight by anything greater than ten per cent from the previous session. Even if the dancer is strong enough to lift greater than ten per cent we must remember that whilst the larger muscle groups may be strong enough we need to spend time strengthening the smaller stabilising muscles and they will fatigue much quicker. Adopt this rule for minimal risk. [7,8]

4. No maximal lifts

Whilst we adopt the ten per cent rule we must also not allow the weight to be increased to an amount were maximal lifts are being completed. No maximal lifts. Keep intensity gradually increasing, but do not increase as far as the athlete's maximal strength lift. [4,5,6}

5. Proper technique

No matter the age, learning technique is the first step in starting any strength programme. Learning technique can be boring and time consuming – most of us want to get straight into the fun stuff and feel like we are actually working out and achieving something. The same applies to the younger athlete, they have a tendency to let their mind wander and spending time teaching technique can be difficult. We must enforce the importance of perfecting technique before any load is added to each exercise, especially for teenagers. [4,5,6]

6. No training without proper supervision

Most, if not all, gyms will have age restrictions on becoming a member. The usual age at which membership is allowed is around sixteen to eighteen. Most would assume that the reason for this is the child is more likely to get injured than the adult. If we have a teenager complete an exercise and an adult complete the same exercise there is nothing to prove the younger person is at a higher risk of injury, given the exercise is completed safely with proper technique and proper supervision. But here lies the problem; a teenager entering a gym is like a child entering a theme park, they are excited at the look of all the equipment and automatically want to start experimenting with exercises and equipment they probably aren't yet ready to handle. A teenager is less knowledgeable and more willing to take risks. It is only for this reason that the younger athlete would be at a greater risk of injury.

We need to manage this risk by ensuring that any younger dancers completing strength work are properly supervised and exercise is conducted under proper instruction. [4,5,6]

7. Individualisation applies to the younger athlete as well as the older athlete

There are many variables a coach will consider when programming for a client, such as their height, weight, training background and previous / current nutritional habits. As teenagers, we still have these variables and these must be taken into consideration. It is common to see groups of children all completing the same type of exercise, but they're kids so this is OK, right? We must factor in the uniqueness of each individual, no matter what age they are. Some kids grow faster than others, meaning they have completely different mechanics in a movement than someone of a different limb length. Some kids are naturally heavier than others, meaning they will have different metabolic qualities to consider. A good coach will take all these variables into consideration when programming for the younger dancers and not simply have them all complete the same exercise. [4,5,6]

8. Overtraining

The teenage body requires extra energy to grow and develop. If overtraining occurs there will be few surplus calories for sustainable growth. We also must remember that the younger the athlete, the less developed the muscle fibres will be. Therefore it will take a lot less to bring a younger dancer's muscle to failure than it would an adult's muscle, where it has had many years of being strengthened as a result of longer term use. [4,5,6]

Strength training for preadolescent dancers (aged around 12 and below)

Over the last twenty-five years, several studies have shown that preadolescent children are capable of safely improving muscle strength with appropriate training regimes. [7] Strength increases twofold between the ages of seven and twelve years, with average values slightly greater in boys. Some would argue that failure to start resistance training before sixteen may be detrimental to playing longevity. [11]

Strength training for pre-adolescent dancers should focus on skills and technique, such as balance, stability and proprioception. Since improvements from strength training come from neuromuscular development in this age group, it is the ideal time to teach coordination and stability. [7] Gains from strength training for preadolescents are generally from the nervous system and motor learning, rather than muscular development and hormones. [10] In other words strength training will improve neural reactions and motor pattern skills responsible for the child's balance, stability and spacial awareness. This research also dismisses concerns that the child would get big, bulky or muscular from resistance training.

In fact, in adults balance can only be regained, not taught – in other words, if you don't already have great balance skills by the age of twelve you may not improve dramatically as an adult. [12]

Alpine skiers have some of the best balance in the world because they are on the slopes from the age of two. Compare that with someone who has been a swimmer from a young age and watch them try to kick a ball when they are older. They will have extremely poor balance and coordination. [12]

If you are a younger dancer or teach a group of younger dancers below the age of twelve, now is the perfect time to dramatically improve their balance and stability skills. It would be a great idea to plan their strength sessions around these two goals.

One option would be to include weekly medicine ball

conditioning workouts to focus not only on stability, but also incorporating some strength and acceleration exercises to help build that solid foundation for their later years, which will help them stay injury free.

Something as simple as shuttle runs around cones will force the dancer into fast rotations followed by quick acceleration of speed to the next cone, teaching them the skills of speed, acceleration, power and sharp rotations across a short distance, all key areas that create a great dancer.

We could even have beginner dancers practise stability movements by getting them to stand on one leg, with the aim of not putting the other foot on the ground, and have a partner gently push them in different directions. This teaches great stability and balance, counteracting the external forces that are trying to push them over.

As dancing is a multi-directional sport these requirements are a must for all dancers and should be incorporated into their weekly training schedules.

This style of strength and conditioning work would be much more beneficial to a child than getting them to complete long aerobic running for general fitness – remember as a younger dancer you are on stage for a very short period of time, so having a great level of endurance will have very little carryover into their performance, whereas learning short-term power, speed, and stability will bring with it great motor skills that will last a lifetime if developed early enough.

Completing stability, balance and speed training can be designed in a group game format. This allows the children to have a lot of fun without even realising they are engaging in strength and stability training.

Summary

There is no minimum age requirement for children undertaking resistance training programmes, but participants should have the emotional maturity to accept and follow directions and should understand the potential benefits and risks associated with strength training. [7]

In a growing number of cases it would appear that the musculoskeletal systems of many young athletes are ill-prepared to handle the demands of their dance practice and competition schedules. [7]. By incorporating moderate strength, stability and balance training into their weekly training you will ensure the child develops a solid foundation. This should all be part of the coaching set up for the aim of the long-term development of our younger dancers and we now know it is safe to do so given we stay within the guidelines.

'TRAINING WITHOUT A PLAN IS LIKE DRIVING A
CAR WITH NO MAP OF WHERE YOU ARE GOING –
WITH NO DIRECTION YOU ARE SIMPLY HOPING
TO ARRIVE AT YOUR DESTINATION BY CHANCE.'
— Lauren Early

CHAPTER SUMMARY

Important points to note:

- Change your training programme every six to eight weeks to avoid a plateau in performance
- Plan your yearly calendar – mark down the important competitions in the year
- Break down your year into three different phases, off season, pre-season and in season, planned around the most important competitions to ensure you peak at the right time
- Have a clear goal to achieve throughout each phase – for example, off season to increase your endurance and in season to increase speed your speed and sharpness
- Change your training as you progress across each phase relevant to the goal
- Include the relevant fitness tests at the beginning and end of each phase to ensure goals were achieved
- Include strength training, balance and stability skills for preadolescent dancers

Chapter 5
Staying injury free

Thankfully the aim of this book is not to teach how to rehabilitate existing injuries. There is an Internet world full of great material, as well as many great therapists, that can assist you in this area. This book is about providing you all with the resources that are not widely available.

My aim in the next chapter is first to teach you the reasons why injuries may occur and then to explain how to ensure you are in the best condition possible to avoid them.

By this point in this book, almost by default we have already taught you many ways of reducing injury risk by structuring your training, changing the type of training you are doing frequently and breaking your training year down into different phases. In this chapter I will take what you have already learnt and expand on it, going into detail about what is actually going on in the body of a dancer when in training or competition. I will discuss the best warm up and cool down methods for injury prevention and also take a look at the use of other sports alongside dance that may increase your injury chances.

At some point in their life most athletes will experience some sort of injury, be it big or small. There are two ways this can happen. The first is as a result of an accident, with no fault attached to the athlete. The second is if something in the body is not mechanically working correctly. In that case the athlete may overcompensate on one side, may not be warmed up sufficiently or may be weak in certain areas, so creating instability in the movement patterns which ultimately results in injury.

In a dance class we are surrounded by injuries waiting to happen and it almost appears as if Irish dancers play a game of *who can last the longest* or *who can fight through the pain the most*. I have seen many dancers, both beginner and advanced, continue dancing despite suffering discomfort, ignoring the warning signs of a potential injury about to occur. Ignoring the warning signs of an injury, or pain, is one of the worst ways to develop long-term pain and dysfunction. Due to the competitive nature of athletes our short-term goals are often seen as more important than our long-term health. We have all experienced this situation at some point, me included, and usually when faced with this we choose to keep on going where possible, ignoring the injury.

There are two ways to deal with injuries:

Rehabilitation and prehabilitation

The term 'rehabilitation' simply means 'recovering an injury back to full health and previous function'.

I like to think of rehabilitation like a beginner going into a gym and trying to squat with a two hundred pound bar on their back (we have all seen this in our local gym). The weight, of course, is too heavy for the novice lifter and they injure the lower back during the lift. A trip to the doctor and many painkillers later the beginner is now pain free and goes back into the gym to try to lift exactly the same two hundred pound bar, maybe because it beat him the first time. He is likely to get injured again, right?

Rehabilitation is like the doctor and the painkillers; it will fix the immediate problem, however, it will not guarantee the injury won't happen again. What is the point of rehabbing an injury if you are going to pay no attention to why it happened and continue to do everything exactly the same as you did prior to the injury? If you do not identify the issue and alter your training accordingly then there is a likelihood the injury will happen again.

That said, finding the cause of the problem is much more difficult than you might think, which is why it is often overlooked. As soon as the athlete is pain-free, they will immediately want to return to training without analysing what is going on in the body to cause the initial injury.

If you have recurring injuries then you need to realise that there is something going on mechanically in the body that is causing this to happen. Do not limit yourself to rehabilitation without actually looking at why you are getting injured in the first place. Is your lower back weak? Is one leg stronger than the other? Are your glutes not working properly? All these issues could develop an issue such as knee pain. Rehab may shift the knee pain, but the main cause of the problem has not changed, meaning once the dancer returns to class there is a high chance the pain will come back again.

A period of rehabilitation can last for anything from around a few weeks to six months, and in more serious cases over a year.

Prehabilitation

The term 'prehabilitation' simply means 'preventing an injury'.

The demand for prehabilitation is the same as rehabilitation. Just as you wouldn't rehab every one of your clients, with their different injuries, in exactly the same way, you shouldn't prehab every dancer identically, as they will each have different requirements. Your tailored programme should initially consist of focusing on the hot spot areas where dancers tend to get injured, but you will need to have an initial assessment of your own physique to determine what needs to be done. An off season prehab programme should target weak and tight muscles, with the goal of fixing any imbalances (more on this later).

Your prehab programme will need to be regularly reviewed and altered as your ability improves and you get stronger, faster and more powerful.

Prehabilitation does not last for any given time period – it should be a staple in your training year round, with most focus placed in the off season.

The bottom line – prehab so you don't need to rehab!

Structural balance / structural imbalance

Structural balance or imbalance is the ratio of strength from one muscle to the next. The closer the ratio of strength across all the muscle groups, the more balanced the body is. The wider the variance of strength across all muscle groups, the less balanced the body will be.

Achieving structural balance is one of the most successful ways to prevent injuries. Imbalances occur when we tend to favour certain muscle groups over others, meaning certain muscles are being used more. As a result these muscles get stronger, develop quicker and leave the underused muscle groups behind. Imbalances increase tension across the joints, muscles and tendons as the ratio of strength between muscle pairings becomes greater.

To make sense of this we can firstly look at muscles and how they function. Without going into great detail, the important point to know is that all muscles work in pairs. An appropriate example would be pairing of the quadriceps and hamstrings, both of which are located in the upper thigh. (Quadriceps are located at the front of the thigh and the hamstrings are located at the back of the thigh.)

As one muscle contracts, the opposing muscle must relax and vice versa. In this example, as the quadriceps is contracted, the hamstring is relaxed. This is exactly how the body is programmed to work, all muscles are in pairs and one will always contract while the other relaxes.

The problem begins when we spend more time contracting a certain muscle and too little time using its opposing muscle. Using one more than the other over long periods of time will undoubtedly lead to imbalances.

Relating this to our example, let's think about what happens if the quadricep spends most of the day contracted and the hamstring spends most of the day relaxed. Of course the quadricep muscle will grow stronger and develop faster, leaving the hamstring behind.

This exact scenario can be related to all dancers. When dancers are training they spend most of the time on their toes, pushing up from the ground. The prime mover in Irish dance is the quadriceps muscle and when we complete a high kick we are usually only stretching our hamstrings; very rarely do we actually strengthen them. This creates a large imbalance in the thigh and is a big problem for most dancers. In fact, this is how we develop all structural imbalances and increase the strength ratio differences between two muscle groups.

What we find is that a dancer's quadriceps muscle is producing too much power for what their hamstring can safely tolerate, resulting in a hamstring pull.

This is a very common injury amongst dancers and yet it is extremely avoidable. Simply spending some time strengthening the hamstring would help reduce the imbalance and reduce injury risk greatly.

Dancing, just like every sport, will favour certain muscle groups over others. In fact every day we will all favour certain muscle groups over others. This is common. However, most other sports will spend time outside of class strengthening the opposing muscle groups that are not being used in their sport to ensure they stay as structurally balanced as possible throughout the year. It is the single best fix for reducing your chances of injury.

Dancers unfortunately very rarely spend any time dedicated to strengthening their opposing muscle groups; very often what we see is just more of the same type of training. The addition of more dance classes, longer dance classes and extra home practices is the common fix if we want to train harder. Unfortunately by adding in more training sessions we only extend the time that the same muscle groups are being worked and the opposing muscle groups are being underworked, expanding the imbalance between the two.

It's time for us to change this. As discussed in previous chapters, I recommend that you all dedicate at least one session per week to strength training, and I strongly recommend you use the time within that strength session to work on your structural balance, focusing on all the opposing muscle groups of the body until you are at a balanced ratio of strength across each group. I then recommend you reintroduce structural balance training at least once per year in your off season phase of training from then on. If your schedule allows, I would even include segments of structural balance training year round.

In the final section of the book I have listed all the major muscle groups that are commonly overused in a dancer. Beside each I have listed the opposing muscle group which is commonly underused. I have also recommended an exercise that you can include for each group to assist you all in your first steps towards achieving structural balance. This programme can be found in the 'Useful information' section at the back of this book.

Now you know what structural balance is, what does it actually look like? Can we see it? Are there any signs that a dancer is imbalanced when performing?

There are many visible movements that show a dancer is structurally imbalanced and, unknown to you, you have seen many of them before. Let's have a look at the mechanics of a dancer and what we should look out for.

Dancing biomechanics

'Biomechanics' simply means looking at or analysing the movements of the body. Dancing biomechanics lets us analyse the movements of the body when we dance.

When observing Irish dancers in competition we can all spot certain movements that are not quite technically perfect, such as poor posture, a forward lean, a twist on top or hands moving from the sides. Effectively we all are checking dancer's biomechanics without realising it every time we watch someone dance.

Observation is the first step in identifying what is going wrong in the mechanics of a certain movement or step. As teachers, parents and dancers I recommend we all spend time watching each other and writing down certain points we pick up during the observation.

The next time you dance, your child dances, or someone in your class dances, have a pen and paper at hand. I want you to write down everything you see in the dancer's movements that many be irregular. Look for points such as hand movements, shoulder rotations, rounded back, twisting hips, bent knees and anything else you can see. Once finished, keep your compiled list on that dancer. This information is a personal analysis of that dancer and the observation should be repeated on a regular basis.

How many of you go through frequent movement analysis in your school to identify any errors that happen each time you dance? The chances are your teacher will already have identified a lot of these key issues in each of you by simply watching you all through every training session. We tend to build up knowledge of what each dancer is known for. I have no doubt you will have dancers in your class known for bad posture, others will be known for hand movements and others will be known for always getting injured. This information is right in front of our faces, but what we fail to do is record it and then identify the cause of these errors.

Unfortunately, simply shouting at someone to stop rocking or stop twisting their hips will not actually fix the problem. The dancer will be trying to do what the teacher is telling them, the problem is they can't – there is something happening mechanically with the dancer that will not allow what you are asking for to happen automatically.

Once we have compiled a list of technical errors for each dancer, we can seek to find out why these errors are continually happening, what is the cause of each of them, and then begin to correct them through structured training.

As well as knowing that all muscles work in pairs, there is also another important role muscles play that as a dancer or teacher you need to be aware of.

For every muscle that creates an action, there is a muscle that has to make a similar reaction. In other words, when a muscle makes a movement, there is an opposite muscle that will try to counteract the movement, if required.

A great example of this is when we walk.

I want you all to stand up and walk several paces forward and back. What do you feel happening as you walk? Remember for every muscle movement there is a similar opposite movement somewhere else. Can you identify it?

Every time your left leg steps forward you should notice your right arm goes forward. When we create movement our bodies are programmed in such a way that they will counteract that movement from the opposite side of the body.

This is how the human body is essentially connected; the nervous system is wired up in opposites. Think about what would happen if the left leg moved and the right side of the body didn't counteract the movement – we would start drifting and turning to the right side, unable to remain in a straight line.

For athletes generating a lot of power from their legs and arms, it is even more important for optimal performance that this counteraction is of equal force.

Let's take, for example, a boxer. When a boxer throws a punch there is a tremendous amount of force leaving the body on one side. If this was not counteracted by the opposite side of the body, the boxer would continue in the plane of movement the arm is going in and spin around. The same could be said for a footballer kicking a ball or a golfer swinging a club, how can they suddenly stop when the ball is hit? The body has to suddenly counteract the power on one side to stop the athlete following on through with the movement, thus keeping them facing in the same direction. If this didn't happen the footballer or golfer would spin right round, with no control to stop the forward momentum.

Athletes in professional sports are great at not showing this counteraction happening simply because they dedicate a lot of time in training to strengthening their opposing muscle groups. (Again, think structural balance.)

Relating this scenario to Irish dancers, a perfect example would be the twisting of the upper body.

It is common knowledge that the majority of dancers will have poor upper body strength compared to their lower body. We know this because dancers spend so much time strengthening the lower body in training, but very little time is spent strengthening the upper body outside of dance class.

If we think back to the walking example, essentially what needs to happen every time a dancer produces a movement from the right leg is that it must be counteracted by the upper and lower back on the left side. Whilst the dancer may be able to counteract it comfortably when walking, unfortunately when dancing the leg is producing much greater power.

In this case of upper body movement, what's happening is that the dancer's lower body is creating too much power for their upper body to counteract, resulting in a twisting movement each time the leg produces power.

To be more specific, if the dancer's right leg is extremely powerful it would be producing more power than the torque of the left upper back can counteract – again resulting in the twist.

If both shoulders are rotating it's a clear sign both legs are too powerful for both sides of the upper back, resulting in a twist across both shoulders.

This is a simple technical issue that can be fixed by spending time strengthening the opposite sides of the body. Even though dancing seems like a lower body sport, if we do not have close to equal strength in the upper body the ability to counteract the power coming from the lower body will be poor and obvious on stage.

In my experience most mechanical issues like this will usually be put down to the dancer having a weak core. I'm sure we have all blamed our core for similar issues. When identifying technical errors like this we must look deeper into the problem. Core strength has become the be all and end all for dancers and whilst it is important, it will not fix issues such as these if you are structurally imbalanced. Having a strong core is certainly part of becoming structurally balanced; however, do not forget about the counteracting and strengthening of the underused opposing muscle groups to fully achieve perfect form on stage. To achieve perfect upper body posture we must train to counteract!

There is no other sport in the world like Irish dancing. As a dancer you must try to keep your upper body completely still while producing power in all directions from the lower body. This goes completely against how the human body is designed. Every time you walk in daily life you are allowing your arm to counteract your leg movement. However, every time you dance you are expected to stop this from happening. Whilst possible, it is a difficult task to achieve, and strengthening your upper body will certainly be a big part of equalling the strength ratio and improving your ability to counteract such power so that it can't be seen by the eye.

As a dance teacher or parent it is not your role to design programmes to fix such issues, but it can be a massive help to your dancers when you spend some time analysing each one and logging their movement errors. Once logged, you can apply everything that you have been taught in this book to fix the errors. In fact, simply by including proper structured phases of training you will go a long way towards fixing them.

The importance of a warm up and cool down

Although a warm up and cool down are equally important, many fail to grasp the great difference between the two and actually don't understand what they are trying to achieve by completing each around their workouts.

The aim of a warm up is to prepare the body for exercise and the movement patterns that are to come. If completed properly, a warm up will improve your heart rate, increase blood flow to the muscles, activate the nervous system and fire up the fast twitch muscle fibres, increasing your speed and contraction times. A warm up will also help release fluid around the joints, which acts as a lubricant for the exercise that is about to come.

The aim of a cool down is to prepare the body to stop exercising and resume normal activity. If completed properly, a cool down will lower your heart rate back down to resting levels, clear any waste products that have built up through the training session, such as lactic acid, reduce post exercise stiffness and kick start the recovery process.

From the above definitions we can clearly see that a warm up and cool down have completely separate and almost opposite goals to each other. With this in mind, when planning your warm up and cool down you must understand that as the goals are different, your warm up and cool down routines must also be different.

If your warm up routine is exactly the same as your cool down routine *(i.e. static stretching before and after exercise)* then you need to reassess your goals and consider why you are completing a warm up and cool down in the first place. Don't do it because you feel you have to, adopt a good routine to receive the full benefits to your performance that each area can bring.

Dynamic vs static stretching

For almost all of us dancers, static stretching is an integral part of our warm up routine; we hold hamstring stretches for around sixty seconds until we feel the muscle stretch out and then it's time to hit the floor. Does this sound like you?

Let's start by looking at the two different types of stretching.

Dynamic stretching is a method of stretching through continual movement. With dynamic stretching the muscle is not held in an end position, rather it is gradually loosened by taking the muscle through its full range whilst moving. Another benefit of dynamic stretching is the fact that it will engage multiple muscle groups at once. This is great as when we are exercising or performing on stage, one muscle does not work by itself, all movements completed by a dancer require multiple joints working at the same time. Essentially through a dynamic warm up process we are getting the muscles to work with each other, best preparing them for what is about to come. This leads to more power and force production.

An example of a hamstring stretch done dynamically would be an exercise such as standing leg swings against a wall. This movement will not only prepare a dancer for something such as a high kick, but will also engage the glutes, hip flexors, lower back and a whole host of stabilising muscle fibres in the one movement – not to mention prepare the hamstring for a fast snap back on competition stage.

Most professional sports have recognised the benefits that a dynamic warm up has to offer pre competition. You just have to look at a soccer, rugby, or NFL team warming up on the pitch to see that dynamic movements are a fundamental part of the team's warm up routine to prepare for competition conditions.

Static stretching is a method used to increase the range of movement through a certain muscle or joint while the body is at rest. If you have poor flexibility and mobility, static stretching can be a great way to actually improve your range of motion. However, as it is completed at rest it is not ideal to carry it out prior to exercise. Whilst seated and holding the stretch, your heart rate will be reduced significantly which will deactivate the nervous system and slow blood flow. This is exactly what we do not want to happen directly before we train or go on stage. However, if your goal is to improve your flexibility then you must incorporate flexibility sessions into your weekly schedule, separate from your training sessions.

Static stretching can specifically target one area with no connection to any other muscle groups. An example of a static stretch would be sitting static on the floor touching your toes. In this movement you feel the hamstring stretch by itself, but it is important to note the rest of the body is inactive and at rest while the stretch is being performed. All sports recognise the benefits that static stretching can bring post workout; however, we have a host of studies that show us just how detrimental static stretching can be to your performance before a workout.

The negative effect of static stretching pre workout

Studies have shown us just how important it is to choose the right kind of stretching before you work out. In-fact, studies have actually gone as far as proving that static stretching before you work out can actually reduce your strength.

Recent studies show us that movement specific dynamic stretching is much more beneficial for sporting performance and highlight the dangers static stretching can bring if completed before you work out.

The first study, conducted at Stephen F. Austin State University, **showed significant strength impairment** in individuals who practiced static stretching before lifting or speed-based exercise, as opposed to those who performed dynamic warm ups (14).

The second study by researchers in Croatia looked at a total of 104 previous studies on stretching and athletic performance. Regardless of age, gender, or fitness level, static stretching before a workout **impaired explosive movement and strength performance** (15).

Research also shows us that dynamic stretches improve force production, explosive power, acceleration and recruitment of fast twitch muscle fibres pre exercise or competition. As all stretching is done through movement, we are essentially preparing the joints and ligaments in the same movement patterns as what's to come.

New research has shown us that static stretching **decreases eccentric strength for up to one hour** after the stretch is held. Static stretching has been shown to **decrease muscle strength by up to nine per cent** for sixty minutes following the stretch and **decrease eccentric strength by seven per cent** followed by a specific hamstring stretch. (16)

Just like dynamic stretching has been shown to improve force production and explosive power, the opposite is also true –

static stretching has been proven to reduce explosive power and force production. Holding a muscle stretch for a long period of time beyond its current range of motion will essentially 'turn off' the fast twitch muscle fibres and make it much harder to fire them up and react with speed once training begins.

Below is a sample layout of a training session that you can adopt immediately to reduce your chances of injury and improve your performance.

Sample layout of a training session

1. Dynamic warm up
2. Speed drills
3. Main component
4. Static stretch cool down

Over-stretching

As much as stretching is important, it is only as important as the amount of flexibility we require to complete a given task. Gymnasts require a great deal of flexibility for optimal sporting performance; however, different sports will require different levels of flexibility.

What most don't realise is that it is actually possible to be too flexible. Let's compare a muscle to an elastic band. An elastic band is tight and difficult to stretch. When you pull the elastic band and let go, it will snap back to its original length quite powerfully. This is because the band has the elastic strength to pull back into position. Now think about what happens if you continually over stretch the elastic band every day. Eventually it will lose its strength and power. Due to this loss the band will appear longer that its original length and will almost resemble a string of spaghetti, loose and weak.

A muscle is no different. What you must realise is that tightness itself is not a bad thing in a muscle. Essentially a tight muscle is a strong muscle and it is tight for a reason. If all we do is stretch the muscle, it will eventually lose its strength and power. If you know someone who is flexible, observe them the next time they dance. They may have perfect form; however, they will almost certainly lack a great deal of power, sharpness and any snap back from a high kick.

If you take a dancer who is extremely flexible and complete a series of strength training phases with them, they will more than likely lose some of their flexibility because as the muscle gets stronger it will also get tighter.

You must not see this as a problem. Sprinters possess an average level of flexibility, but they ensure it is sufficient so as not to inhibit the movement patterns required of the sport. A sprinter does not seek to be overly flexible as they need to retain a certain degree of muscle tightness for speed and strength. On the other hand competitive Irish dancers have adopted a mindset that they must be as flexible as a gymnast or a ballerina. You do not need to be able to complete the splits to be a great Irish dancer, and as for a ballerina, just look at how little power and sharpness they have in their movements.

Most of us could do with improving our flexibility, just ensure it is not done before you work out and be certain you are not over-stretching. Be sure to maintain the degree of flexibility that is required for specific Irish dance movements and not only will you prevent injuries, you will be a strong, sharp and powerful dancer.

Foam rolling and deep tissue massage

Foam rolling is a self-massage technique that can reduce the risk of injury when performed correctly. Just like getting a deep tissue massage from a therapist, foam rolling will allow you to apply your own degree of pressure and control the movement yourself.

Foam rolling can be done with many different items, such as rolling pins, cricket, lacrosse or golf balls, your own hands and, of course, foam rollers themselves.

The principle of self-massage and deep tissue therapy is the application of pressure to specific points in the body, aiding recovery and returning the muscle to its normal length and function. These specific points are also known as trigger points or knots within the muscle.

Releasing knots and trigger points will restore proper movement patterns and ensure flexibility and elasticity are regained. Essentially the muscle is ready to perform again when required.

Working out any knots in the muscle tissue can be quite a painful experience, but once completed correctly will return proper blood flow to the muscle, speeding up the recovery process.

There is a lot of debate about whether there are any disadvantages to foam rolling prior to a workout. Until there is clear research proving what is the best time, we should adopt a common sense approach. In my experience foam rolling before a workout can help release the pressure in a muscle to aid in achieving a full range of movement, releasing any adhesions in the muscle that may be restricting mobility. However, if we do choose to foam roll pre workout we must ensure it is short in duration and does not focus on any one area for longer than sixty seconds.

If you require a full deep tissue massage or an extended foam roll I recommend scheduling it for your rest day or after your workout. Deep tissue work that targets the muscle for an extended period of time (thirty to sixty minutes) will soften the muscle fibres too much, restricting their ability to fire up and produce sufficient speed or power directly after the massage. It will essentially turn off the muscle fibres. It is for this reason that you would not get a sports massage or complete an extensive foam roll prior to a workout.

It is personal choice if you wish to foam roll for a brief period before a workout; however, foam rolling after your workout and on rest days should be a staple in every athlete's training schedule.

Limiting the use of external sports and different types of dance to decrease your injury risk

Earlier in the book we read about the use of external sports to improve dance performance. It used to be widely recommended that dancers should train in other sports in order to train in different movement patterns that in turn would help with imbalances and reduce the injury risk in the athlete's main sport. However, there is a fine line between which sports can actually benefit us in terms of improving our Irish dance performance and unfortunately most get their selection wrong.

We tend to see a lot of dancers change across to other types of dance in order to try to improve certain weaknesses that other dancing styles might address. A good example would be Irish dancers going to ballet classes to improve flexibility. Whilst this may be great short term, there tends to be several issues and bad habits that the dancer may then adopt in the process. When dancers cross over to ballet we tend to see them develop the infamous ballet gap between the thighs and a general float across the dance floor, losing aggression and power. (Think back to over-stretching and loss of strength.)

Just because there are other styles of dancing does not mean they will improve your performance. There are different types of dancing for a reason – they're all different. Different styles of dance require different speeds, different movement patterns, different energy systems, different time durations, a range of flexibility requirements and differing intensity levels.

My advice would be to keep any external training as close to your dance requirements as possible.

We already know that dancers are completing too much aerobic work, so that would be a key consideration in selecting other sports to use alongside Irish dancing. As a dancer you would want to opt for anaerobic based sports at least pre and in season, to be training in the same energy requirements as your main sport.

Whilst aerobic work is a huge problem for dancers, another issue we commonly see that comes along with this is the type of equipment being used to complete that aerobic work.

A great example would be when dancers cycle to improve their fitness. The short-term benefits of cycling for dancers are that there is less impact on the body, which makes it perfect as part of a rehabilitation process. But what are the issues with long-term cycling for dancers if they are only completing it from an improved fitness perspective?

Posture

The problem with cycling is that we need to look at the postural position it puts the dancer in for the prolonged period of time they are cycling. As a dancer we need to stand tall on stage with great posture and retracted shoulder blades. We must have great core contraction and develop great lift through the hips off the ground.

The problem with cycling is that if you look at how you are seated on the bike it is extremely counterproductive for what we need as a dancer.

Being seated on a bike forces your hips into an extremely tight position. You naturally would have an extreme forward lean with a rounded back and rounded shoulders as you reach for the handlebars. Due to this excessive lean you get very little core activation and, as you are crunched over, it inhibits any proper core contractions. As you are in a seated position on the bike your glutes (bum muscles) are inactive as they are resting on a padded seat. If we then look at the pedal motion in the legs as you cycle, you only ever press the pedal down, you never pull it back up, meaning the quadriceps are getting overworked and the hamstrings get very little work.

Now, as we know from the structural balance section, dancers are already imbalanced in the thigh, so it would seem cycling will only worsen this issue. On top of that dancers already struggle with extremely tight hips, poor posture, overworked quadriceps and a weak lower back, so completing extra exercise on a bike to improve 'fitness' would more than likely be more detrimental to your Irish dance performance than beneficial. Also, if you choose to cycle, then unless it is speed track cycling it would more than likely be over great distances, thus training in the aerobic threshold and developing the wrong kind of fitness – not that which we require.

This is just one example of how external sports can be detrimental to the requirements of an Irish dancer and many more examples could be made across other sports. Be careful when selecting external sports to complete and be sure to check the movement patterns against those of Irish dancing as it may be detrimental to your performance. If dancing is your primary focus I recommend you include only sprinting and strength training alongside your regular dance classes as these are safe options and require similar movements to those of Irish dancing.

The use of ankle weights and weighted vests in Irish dance

Think back to the first time you ever learned to kick a ball, it would have taken you many attempts to learn to kick it with complete accuracy and force as your body struggled to find the movement pattern required. Now look at a professional soccer player, they can kick the ball in exactly the same spot time after time with little effort. They have repeated the same motion so many times that it just happens automatically.

When starting something new your body will have to ingrain the new movement patterns required for that action. Imagine you suddenly decide to play golf, initially your swing would be extremely inaccurate; however, the more you practise the more efficient it becomes until eventually, just like the footballer, you are able to hit the ball with precision on every swing, as it becomes second nature.

As dancers most of you will have spent many years learning the difficult mechanics of each movement required and now most of you can probably do them effortlessly, which is great. But let's consider what would happen if we suddenly disrupted the mechanics of the movement somehow. What do you think would happen if I added a weighted vest to your body and made you complete a full dance ... would the automatic process happen? You will more than likely be knocked out of sync and your movements will be unstable, unbalanced and inaccurate. It would be like learning to dance all over again.

There is a fine line when using equipment such as ankle weights, wrist weights and weighted vests. Whilst these items will increase the difficulty of your training and make you stronger, they will also completely change the mechanics of the movements you have ingrained in your brain over the years.

If you put a wrist weight on a boxer, he will almost certainly hit the punch bag at a different angle and position, even when trying to hit the same spot.

Putting an ankle weight on a footballer will almost certainly force the player to kick the ball in an unwanted position and angle.

An Irish dancer is no different, and the use of weighted equipment must not be allowed when practising specific dance movements as it will completely inhibit the normal pattern of the movement and knock the body completely out of its natural alignment. Doing so would force the body to adjust to new angles and learn to develop a new way to complete the movement, only for you to take the weight off so your stabilising muscles are left confused as to which is the most efficient path to take. Do not knock your movements out of sync.

I wouldn't completely avoid the use of weighted equipment,

however. Using weighted equipment can be massively beneficial in external training, such as hill sprints. I have used weighted vests with dancers in the off season phase to build a solid level of base strength. I have also had dancers sprint with sled pulls on a track to develop greater drive and acceleration across short distances in the in season phase.

Please continue to use this equipment to assist in your training, but remember the importance of not using it when performing your main dance patterns. Ultimately you would not have this extra load on competition day, therefore my advice would be for you to keep dance training as close to competition conditions as possible.

If anyone experiences excessive weight loss or weight gain, this can essentially be the same as adding a weighted vest to your performance. Weight gain or weight loss can change the mechanics of movement patterns you have developed, therefore any weight gain or weight loss required by an athlete must be done in a controlled manner to allow the stabilising muscles to adapt to the new weight and adjust your mechanics accordingly.

My hope is that this chapter has given you all an insight into the best prevention methods to help you stay injury free. There is one final piece missing in your quest to having an injury free career: nutrition. Your nutrition will play a massive role in fuelling your workouts, the recovery process and keeping you injury free. Now you have learnt how to train properly, how to plan your year into different training phases and the best training techniques you need to adopt to stay injury free, are you ready to learn how to eat for optimal athletic performance???

'ASK YOURSELF IF WHAT YOU ARE DOING TODAY IS GETTING YOU CLOSER TO WHERE YOU WANT TO BE TOMORROW.' — Lauren Early

CHAPTER SUMMARY

Important points to note:

- **Prehab so you don't have to rehab!**
- **All muscles work in pairs**
- **Strengthen the underused muscle groups**
- **The aim of a warm up is to prepare the muscle for the movement patterns that will follow**
- **Avoid static stretching before your workout**
- **Be careful when using other sports to assist in your dance performance**
- **Limit the use of weighted equipment to external training**

PART 3

NUTRITION

Overview

In an Internet world full of fitness gurus offering so much different advice, trying to educate yourself on the best nutritional practices for your goals is often a headache. With no shortage of advice out there – and certainly no shortage of bad advice – it can be daunting when trying to eat right, especially considering most of us don't even know what 'right' is. Eating right for an athlete is different from eating right to lose weight. Every paper, magazine and advert promotes different methods, from weight loss shakes to juice diets, and the latest fad diets.

The truth is there are no such things as bad foods, good foods or the best diet. There are simply foods that are better for your goals and foods that are detrimental to them, but you must first determine what your goals are. Before seeking nutritional advice it is important you know exactly what your goal is so that the advice you receive is relevant to that goal.

For example, there are food choices that can be made for fat loss, but the complete opposite choices are probably made for enhancing athletic performance. If you are a fat loss client reading an athletic performance article you will be told why you need to have a high carbohydrate diet to fuel your performance, but this is essentially not what you need at the moment. It's not bad advice, it's just geared towards the wrong demographic. Similarly, if you are an athlete looking for performance nutrition advice and you come across an article on how to become healthy and lose body fat aimed at the general public, this advice will almost certainly limit calorie intake and carbohydrate intake, which is the exact opposite of what you need. And of course there is the advice in the middle, that is just complete rubbish no matter what category you fall into.

In order for me to effectively teach you the fundamental basics of establishing your own nutritional requirements, I must first briefly discuss the food groups and their roles within the body. There are certain points you must learn to enable you to understand which foods you require to improve your performance, and why. Of course, if you want to improve your diet in any way it is important you understand what foods play which roles within the body.

In chapter 6 I will explain all the food groups, their roles, and how to calculate your calorie requirement for optimal performance, weight loss or weight gain.

In chapter 7 I will teach you how to calculate your daily calorie requirement relative to your own specific needs. I will also teach you how to effectively use a calorie tracker application to monitor your daily calorie intake.

In chapter 8 I will teach you how to put all this information together and fundamentally fuel your performance. I will teach the parents how to help their young athletes choose better food sources and I will assist the teacher in ways to hold their dancers accountable for their nutrition and recovery outside of class!

(This book is aimed at parents, teachers and younger dancers rather than fitness industry professionals, and so I have aimed to give you the basics you need to know in as clear and simple a way as possible.)

Chapter 6
Nutrition – the basics

Food groups and their roles within the body

Macronutrients – proteins, carbohydrates and fats

Nutrients are required for human survival. All nutrients can be divided into three different groups depending on their macronutrient content *(that is, on what they provide to the body)*. The three groups are proteins, carbohydrates and fats. The primary role of a macronutrient is to provide the body with energy and calories; however, the amount of calories each provides differs.

Proteins

We need to think of proteins as building blocks. Just like bricks are required to build the structure of a house, protein is required to build the structure of the human body. Protein plays many major roles in the body. Our skin, nails, hair and all of our organs are made from proteins. The immune system, digestive system and our blood is all is reliant on proteins to function properly.

From a sports perspective athletes need protein for the regeneration and repair of damaged and broken down muscle tissue, ensuring full recovery from one training session to the next. If our diet is lacking in protein, so too will be our recovery capabilities be lacking. The important thing to know about protein that it is a very poor form of energy for the body; it is better used for its main role of tissue repair and regeneration.

The body will not store protein for use at a later time. In other words, if we decided to eat our daily protein content in one meal it would not be stored throughout the day for ongoing use; instead we would use what we needed initially and the rest would be digested as waste products, leading to a requirement for more protein later that day. This brings about the requirement for regular protein consumption throughout the day, preferably with every meal, especially for trained athletes.

As athletes we are constantly in a state of repair. You can imagine if we only ate one meal per day with protein (*the usual example is a meat source with dinner)*; apart from that window of opportunity there would be very little recovery across the rest of the day.

Vegetarians also suffer from inadequate protein intake and usually have to resort to incomplete sources of protein, which will provide very little in comparison to complete sources such as animal proteins.

The body will break down protein as a fuel source in the

absence of other forms of energy *(carbohydrates and fats)*. In this scenario the body will degenerate *(break down)* existing muscle mass in order to fuel the body. If we look at a marathon runner, these athletes usually possess a low percentage of muscle mass as the body essentially feeds on itself to fuel the long workouts.

For athletes in sports that require great speed and strength it is important to limit the loss of muscle tissue and strength by ensuring the body is well fuelled for training and competition. A body full of energy will be able to keep any available protein to complete its primary role of enhancing full recovery and repair of muscle tissue. From my observations and experience with the Irish dancers that I have worked with, protein is currently one of the nutrients most lacking in a dancer's diet, something which is clearly shown in their daily food logs.

I have provided you with a sample list of protein sources below:

COMPLETE PROTEIN SOURCES *(animals)*	INCOMPLETE PROTEIN SOURCES *(plants)*
Beef	Grains
Fish	Nuts
Poultry	Seeds
Dairy Products	Legumes / Beans / Peas

Protein contains four calories per gram

Carbohydrates

Carbohydrates are the preferred energy source for the body. When carbohydrates enter body they are converted into glucose *(blood sugars)*. Glucose can be rapidly sent to muscle cells providing a fast release of energy.

Though carbohydrates are not essential for survival, they are essential for optimal function and performance, which is why carbohydrates should be a staple in an athlete's diet, especially those that are involved in speed and power based sports *(this increases the demand for fast release energy)*.

Carbohydrates come in three forms: complex *(starches)*, simple *(sugars)* and fibre *(also spelt as fiber)*.

For now we will focus on simple and complex carbohydrates. *(There's more on fibre later in this section.)*

All carbohydrates eventually get converted into glucose in the body; however, it is the speed at which they are digested that separates the two. Starchy carbohydrates *(see example list)* are broken down much more slowly than sugary carbohydrates and are a slow release form of energy. Sugary carbohydrates *(see example list)* enter the bloodstream rapidly and are a form of fast release energy. Both types will raise blood sugar levels, but complex carbs will be digested at a slower rate than sugars, which digest rapidly into the bloodstream. Fast digestion is great if the body requires energy fast; however, if the sugars are not required for immediate use, we get a peak in sugar levels followed by low sugar levels as the body clears the bloodstream of excess sugar, usually clearing too much in the confusion, which leads to further sugar cravings. This is why when you eat something sugary you tend to feel hungry again quite soon after.

Even though sugars are more important for the athlete than the general public, intake must be strategically timed and sugars consumed when they are most needed *(post workout)*. Consumption should be controlled at all other points in the day.

Unlike protein, carbohydrates can be stored as fuel for use at a later point. This is great as we know if we run out of the energy stored in the muscle the body can then tap into its reserves.

Athletes require a high carbohydrate diet *(given the athlete is at optimal body fat levels)*. Carbohydrates improve athletic performance, delay the onset of fatigue and allow the athlete to compete at greater intensity for longer periods.

The relationship between body fat and carbohydrate consumption

Body fat is the overconsumption of energy that has subsequently been stored as a reserve fuel source. The purpose of body fat is stored fuel that can be reverted back to an energy source for use when required. This storage mechanism is a survival response controlled by the body to ensure we have a backup supply of energy if required.

If we understand how and why we store body fat it is easy to see how the majority of the population ends up overweight. The human body can only store a limited amount of glycogen, so any excess glucose is stored as body fat. The body stores excess carbohydrates as energy; however, instead of tapping into this extra energy supply we simply continue to eat more carbohydrates, resulting in more overspill and further storage of body fat. Simply put, there is no requirement to use the stored energy as we continue to put too much in.

Understanding how much carbohydrate you require is a complex subject as each individual's requirements differ greatly. *(This is not a topic for an entry level book.)* However, a general guide is that the leaner you are, the more carbohydrates you can have. The higher your body fat percentage, the less tolerant you are to carbohydrates and you could have less in your diet. For optimal performance we need to find the correct energy balance – it needs to be enough to fuel your performance without causing you to gain excess body fat.

The key with carbohydrates is to know when to use them to your advantage. If you are not at an optimal level of body fat, start by including them at strategic times in the day such as around training times to fuel your workouts and decrease the chance. I have provided you with a sample carbohydrate list below.

COMPLEX CARBOHYDRATE SOURCES (starches)	SIMPLE CARBOHYDRATE SOURCES (sugars)
Rice	Cake
Wholegrain Bread	Candy
Beans	Soft Drinks
Wholewheat Pasta	Fruit Juice
Potatoes	Corn Syrup
Peas	Honey
Bread – Wholemeal	Bread – made with white flour
Pasta – Wholemeal	Pasta – made with white flour
Root Vegetables	Jams
Fruit*	Fruit*

* (Since fruit is composed of fructose it passes through the liver slowly and can sometimes be known both as a complex carbohydrate and a simple carbohydrate. Regardless of the speed it digests, we already know the great benefits it will bring.)

Carbohydrates contain four calories per gram

Fibre

Dietary fibre can be found in the plants that we eat. The fibre is the nutrient in the plants that does not break down when consumed and so passes through the body undigested.

Because of its non-digestible properties fibre helps cleanse the digestive tract as it leaves the body, improving digestion in the gut. A diet low in fibre may lead to digestive problems such as stomach bloat or indigestion. Whilst it is important to consume enough fibre daily for optimal health and digestion, a diet that is too high in fibre or in which fibre is quickly and dramatically increased can also cause digestive problems. A slow increase will allow the body to adapt to the new levels of fibre.

Eating foods high in fibre will keep you feeling fuller for longer, a great way to keep control of food cravings and the over consumption of foods. Eating fibre with carbohydrate foods also helps slow down the rate at which it is digested into the body, therefore slowing the rate at which blood sugar levels rise. For example, eating some green vegetables with potatoes at dinner will slow down the digestion, stabilising blood sugar levels more effectively.

Fibre can be broken down into two types – soluble fibres and insoluble fibres. Put simply, soluble fibres dissolve in water, insoluble fibres do not. Regardless of this difference both types of fibre play an equally critical role in our health and digestive process. I have provided you with a sample list of fibre sources below.

FIBRE SOURCES (soluble & insoluble)	
Oatmeal	Dark Leafy Vegetables
Lentils / Beans / Peas	Fruit

Flaxseeds	Green Vegetables
Nuts	Whole Wheat
Potato Skins	Whole Grains
Berries	Seeds
Oat Bran	Figs

Fats

Fats play a major role in overall health and function in the human body. Though carbohydrates are the primary fuel source in the body, fats can be seen as a reserve fuel source for times when carbohydrates are not available. Despite having developed a bad reputation within the health and fitness industry, not all fats are bad.

Fats can be found in several forms: polyunsaturated, monounsaturated, saturated and trans-unsaturated fats. To keep it simple we will divide them into two groups: fats that we should eat and fats that we should avoid.

Fats, such as polyunsaturated, monounsaturated, and now even saturated fats, are all deemed to be healthy and necessary food sources. These fats play many different roles in the body. From an athletic performance perspective fats are crucial for making hormones. Hormones such as testosterone are responsible for muscle mass, strength, speed and power. Fats also provide us with a backup energy source and help to absorb vitamins within the body *(fat soluble)*. For general health, fats protect your major organs, promote optimal brain and cell function, and maintain healthy skin, nails and hair.

What type of fats should we avoid?

Trans-unsaturated fats are found in processed foods and partially hydrogenated oils are found in fried foods. These fats offer zero benefits within the body and are included in foods such as cookies, cakes and doughnuts to extend their shelf life.

What about saturated fats?

Saturated fats, found in foods such as butter, bacon and eggs, are not what they have been made out to be in recent years. We are now seeing more and more doctors recommending a higher fat diet for weight loss in those people who cannot tolerate carbohydrates very well, although in the past many believed that saturated fats were the leading cause of heart disease and rising cholesterol levels. I have explained how this has all changed below.

The cholesterol myth

Many nutrition 'facts' start out purely as rumour until they have been so widely circulated that they are accepted as truth. In fact, when we look at each of these we generally find that there is just a little scientific research to back the theories up, despite the fact that they are mere myths.

One of the biggest misleading subjects ever in nutrition is that of the cholesterol / heart disease myth. For years many believed that a diet including red meats and eggs could lead to heart disease and raise cholesterol levels in the body. We avoided these foods, believing we were improving our health, and all this happened despite there being no solid scientific research to back it up – it was based purely on the strength of widely circulated myths or poor quality studies.

We have all heard that eating cholesterol and saturated fats raises cholesterol levels in the blood. We also grew up surrounded by information telling us that high cholesterol in the blood is the cause of heart disease … until now.

What is cholesterol?

Cholesterol is a fat-like substance that's found in all cells of the body. Your body needs cholesterol to make hormones, vitamin D and stomach bile to help digest food (1). It's also crucial for the development of babies. So far so good, right?

Cholesterol comes in two forms. Low-density lipoprotein (LDL) cholesterol is deemed to be the 'bad' form, with high-density lipoprotein (HDL) cholesterol deemed to be the 'good' form. The differences lie in the roles they play within the body and it is important to keep a healthy balance of HDL to LDL. So how do we do this?

Your body can make all the cholesterol it needs. However, roughly twenty-five per cent of cholesterol comes from our diet and seventy-five per cent is produced by the body itself. We now know that dietary cholesterol – the cholesterol in the foods that we eat – is poorly absorbed by the body. On top of that, our body needs to maintain a certain level of cholesterol, something which is tightly regulated. So what happens when we reduce our cholesterol intake through foods? Our bodies produce more. And what happens when our cholesterol intake goes up? Our bodies produce less!

What about saturated fat increasing cholesterol?

Short-term studies lasting only several weeks show saturated fats causing slight increases in cholesterol levels within the body. (2,3) However, this could be due to the body requiring longer to regulate the influx of saturated fats, because long-term studies completed show us that there is no significant association between the consumption of saturated fats and blood cholesterol levels. (There is one exception, but that could only manage to show a very weak association.) (2,4)

Saturated fat and heart disease *(non-cholesterol related)*

There were also those who thought it was possible for saturated fat to contribute to heart disease without it being cholesterol related; however, 'a large study involving close to 350,000 participants showed no association between saturated fat and heart disease'. (2,5) A Japanese study confirmed the findings and also showed that those who ate more saturated fats had a lower risk of a stroke. (2,6)

To sum up, we all respond to cholesterol in different ways; however, long-term it should balance out to very little overall increase or decrease. Moving forward we are now all acknowledging the poor connection to this myth and safely including these foods back in our diets again. Long gone are the days of just eating egg whites and avoiding egg yolks, red meats and butter. Eggs are one of the few near perfect foods that we have available to us. They provide us with the highest quality protein and a host of vitamins. Eat them whole, enjoy some red meats and maintain healthy cholesterol levels.

Whilst carbohydrates and protein contain four calories per gram, **fats contain nine calories per gram,** making fats extremely calorie dense. This is why a small portion of fats such as nuts can actually be quite high in calories.

Micronutrients

Vitamins and minerals

Micronutrients are made up of vitamins and minerals, which are required only in small quantities within the body. Vitamins and minerals are crucial for our health, growth, heartbeat, regulation of metabolism, optimal function and performance.

All foods contain micronutrients; however, due to poor dietary habits, stress and over usage of these nutrients it is important to know what they are so that we can supplement appropriately.

Vitamins

There are thirteen vitamins in total. Nine of these are water soluble vitamins, meaning they digest easily in water within the body. The other four are fat soluble vitamins and are only digestible and absorbed with fat in body. (Hence the requirement to consume healthy fats in your diet.) I have provided you with a sample list of vitamins below.

VITAMINS (water soluble)	VITAMINS (fat soluble)
8 x Vitamin B types, Vitamin C	Vitamin A, D, E, K

Minerals

Minerals cannot be made in the body, therefore we must obtain them from the foods that we eat.

Minerals are responsible for building strong bones (i.e. calcium – a well-known mineral), controlling the fluid and electrolyte balance within the body to try maintain safe levels, and they are involved in the processes that turn the food we eat into energy for use in the muscle.

There are around fifteen minerals found in the human body; however, the most well-known minerals are arguably zinc, magnesium, potassium, sodium and calcium.

Hydration – how much should we drink?

Water is massively important for general health, but especially for optimal performance.

We need to see water like a taxi – water is responsible for transporting energy into the muscle cells. Water cannot directly increase energy as it does not contain any; however, now we know that it transports it in the body it's clear to see how people feel like they have much more energy as soon as they drink water.

There are many different theories as to how much water we should drink, but the standard advice is around six to eight glasses of water per day. This advice is based around the needs of an average person with normal activity levels, which of course can vary greatly from one person to the next, depending upon how much they sweat, the climate that they live in and their actual activity level. However, I don't know of any dancers or athletes that could be described as an average person with a normal activity level.

An athlete's body uses fuel more efficiently, trains harder, dehydrates quicker, sweats a lot more and loses quite a lot of salts and electrolytes each day, not to mention their bodies are in recovery mode almost twenty-four hours per day.

Taking this all into consideration, I recommend that we should all aim to drink around three litres or 105 fluid ounces of water per day. If you live in a warmer climate or naturally sweat a lot, you could consider increasing this amount.

I would also advise athletes to think about the electrolytes they lose when exercising. Salts that are lost during exercise need to be replaced. If you have ever experienced headaches or cramping (or both) during or after training, it is usually down to dehydration causing an offset electrolyte balance.

It is possible to get electrolytes from sports drinks and they are a great choice to include around your workout; however, if you want to replace lost fluids throughout the day and don't want all the sugar that comes with a sports drink, consider sprinkling some coloured salts into your water and avoid the unnecessary sugar intake.

Sodium is a mineral that will help retain water in the muscle, thus decreasing the rate of fatigue, dehydration and cramping.

Keeping the body alkaline

The human body will perform optimally when it is in an alkaline state. Eating a poor diet with processed and fried foods will turn the body very acidic. On top of that we compete in a lactic acid based sport. Training several times per week increases the amount of lactic acid produced within the body, therefore you can imagine how acidic an athlete with a poor diet can actually get.

There are many ways to help flush out the toxins and improve our alkaline balance, such as cleaning up or diet *(discussed later)*. However, we can also do this through hydration and the use of citrus fruits. Fruits such as lemons or limes may seem very acidic, but they are actually very alkaline once inside the body. These fruits also have diuretic properties to help flush out toxins.

Squeezing fresh lemon or lime juice into your water throughout the day not only decrease the body's acidity but also helps flavour the water, which improves our chances of drinking the required amounts.

Drinking tap water

Whilst tap water is free and keeps us alive, it is treated with chlorine to kill bacteria, Unfortunately chlorine cannot separate the good bacteria and bad bacteria, and so kills all the bacteria in the water. It also affects our stomach bacteria, which through time can cause digestion problems.

For the general public it may not be so much of a problem and certainly it's nothing to be overly concerned about; however, for athletes who drink a lot of water daily this can build up over time. I recommend trying to drink bottled or filtered water where possible. With bottled water I recommend you try not to refill the same bottle; change the bottle regularly or purchase a BPA free bottle. BPA (bisphenol A) is a toxic chemical that can dissolve from the plastic into the water over time. This chemical disrupts hormones within the body. Whilst it is not life threatening, we might as well avoid it, especially as optimal health and performance are our main goals.

To sum up – aim to drink around three litres or 105 fluid ounces of fresh water per day. Add some salts around training sessions, and more if you experience headaches or cramping throughout the day. Aim to choose bottled or filtered water more often than tap water where possible and if refilling, aim to change your plastic bottles regularly or purchase a BPA free bottle.

Supplementation – the foundation five

There are endless amounts of supplements for sale everywhere you look. Whilst it is important to ensure you are not deficient in any of the main areas, I have given you my top five supplements below. These supplements make up a base level of supplementation for everyone I work with, no matter the goal. The supplements listed make my top five priority list simply because they are responsible for the playing the most roles in the body. If we are ensuring we are getting enough of the required list below, we will be going a long way towards improving our health and performance.

1. Multivitamin

Role in body: supplementing with a multivitamin ensures there is no deficiency of any essential nutrients required by the body that may be depleted through exercise or other activity.

2. Magnesium and zinc

Role in body: magnesium promotes better sleep, lower stress levels and therefore reduced cortisol and oestrogen levels. Zinc has been shown to increase our natural testosterone levels by inhibiting the conversion of testosterone to oestrogen, which will help positively balance fat to muscle ratio.

3. Omega 3 fish oils

Role in body: reduces inflammation, improves blood flow and reduces blood pressure. Studies also show it helps with preventing heart disease. Fish oils improve insulin sensitivity, resulting in the lowering of body fat in the abdomen.

4. Probiotics

Role in body: provides good bacteria, helps with the digestion of food and assists in the repair of any gut issues.

5. Vitamin D3

Role in body: supports immune function, regulates blood sugar, assists fat burning and muscle function (less vitamin D will be required by people who spend a lot of time in the sun. Even if you live in a sunny country, you actually have to be in the sun to absorb it!)

Now that we know what each of the food groups are, how do we know how much of these we actually need in our diet and how many calories we require? Let's move on to chapter 7!

'WITHOUT FIRSTLY KNOWING YOUR GOALS IT IS IMPOSSIBLE TO KNOW WHICH FOODS YOU MUST EAT – CHOOSE YOUR GOAL, THEN YOUR FOODS.'
– Lauren Early

CHAPTER SUMMARY

Important points to note:

- **Protein is responsible for growth and recovery**
- **Carbohydrates are responsible for energy**
- **Fibre is needed for digestion**
- **Healthy fats are needed for hormones, health and function in the body**
- **Ensure adequate hydration each day**
- **Include a baseline of supplements in your diet to cover any potential deficiencies**

Chapter 7
Calculating your daily calorie requirement

Overview

Tracking your calories has never been easier, there are so many online programs and android apps that we can use to track our foods at the touch of a button. Many more of us are beginning to log our foods, which is great; however, if your knowledge of nutrition is limited there are several problems. Once you log your food for the day the app will generate the total amount of calories consumed that day, along with a breakdown of the food. In other words, how much of your intake was made up of proteins, carbohydrates and fats. This is great information, but once we have gone beyond our current scope of nutrition knowledge, we don't really know what to do with the data or how to change it, right?

If we don't know how many calories we should be eating then we don't know if the amount the app told us we have eaten is too low or too high. And if we don't know how much of that number should be made up of carbohydrates, proteins and fats, then again we don't know if the ratios we have just eaten are right or wrong.

Some of the newer software is now trying to build in this data so it can work it out for you; however, in my experience it is inaccurate and if the user doesn't understand the equations, it leads to confusion and loss of interest.

In the next section I am going to help you work out your calorie requirement based on your activity levels. Once you have this number we will then discuss the appropriate breakdown of each food group, so by the end of this chapter you'll know exactly how much food you require, what food groups you should eat and in what amounts.

Understanding your metabolic rate (BMR)

Your BMR represents the total number of calories your body requires each day just to survive. For example, if you were to do nothing but stay in bed all day, this is the amount of calories your body requires at rest to stay alive and keep all your organs working efficiently.

Your BMR includes calories for basic functions such as the beating of your heart, expanding your lungs, growing your hair, generating heat in the body and even blinking! The first step is finding out what your BMR actually is. Once you know your estimated number we first must ensure we have sufficient calories going in each day to cover all these vitally important tasks. Remember, this does not include extra calories for work or training, this is simply to survive!

There are many people under eating, people who eat less than their BMR requires, meaning the body has to slow down its energy expenditure. Let's say, for example, my BMR is 1500 calories, but I only consume 1000 calories. What happens? Well, my body is faced with two choices; if it continues to burn 1500 calories and I am only eating 1000 calories, eventually I would die, because my body is using more calories than are going in. The other choice the body has is to slow down your metabolism so that you are now only using 1000 calories per day to survive. As your metabolism slows down, so does everything you do. If you ever see or know someone that under eats I can guarantee you they will always be cold in the mornings and they won't grow much body hair very quickly. I want you to shake their hand, and I can guarantee you it will be cold. Why? There are not enough calories to complete all the jobs within the body, the calories they are eating must first go to the most important jobs such as pumping their heart and lungs, leaving little energy left to complete jobs such as creating body heat and hair growth. This person will actually even blink and talk less than those who eat above their BMR needs.

This is why someone who under eats for weight loss will never reach their desired end result. The human body is extremely smart and, for our own benefit, it will do everything it can to protect us and help us to survive. It does not care if you have abs or look great in a bikini. If we eat less than we require our metabolism will slow to match what is coming in to what is going out, thus slowing the weight loss.

Another important point to mention is that those who eat below the BMR requirements will lose scale weight, but a lot of this will be muscle tissue loss. Muscle is an active tissue and uses calories each day to stay alive and function. Fat on the other hand is not an active tissue, meaning it uses none of our calorie pot each day. Thus when we under eat, the body will get rid of as much muscle tissue as it can afford to, simply because it will save extra calories each day for the more important tasks. For those who diet but do not strength train, you need to be extremely careful of muscle loss. How do you know if the weight you are losing is fat tissue and not muscle tissue? If you are losing strength as you are losing weight, that is a very good indication that you are losing muscle. Ultimately weight loss is about being leaner and healthier, you should be stronger at the end of your journey than you were at the start. Unfortunately many people who crash diet without strength training will actually be much weaker at the end of the process and will find it impossible to shift the lasts bits of fat, especially females. Why do you think the last bits of unwanted fat seem to be on the hips and thighs? As a female your body will do everything it can to protect for reproduction, therefore your body will continually shift the lasts bits of unwanted fat to these areas to protect you. If you are under eating you will find it extremely hard to shift this and you must increase your calorie intake to put your body into a positive state.

As athletes we are asking so much more of our body than the average person, therefore it is even more crucial that we are getting enough calories to cover all our essential needs first.

The bottom line is no matter whether you are a dancer, teacher or parent, your number one priority is your health. Do not make your body work harder than it needs to do, and do ensure you provide it with enough fuel to do its job … its job – for us!

There is a simple equation we can use involving our height, weight, gender and age that will determine our basal metabolic rate. I have provided you with a website address below directing you to a BMR calculator that will complete the calculation for you. There are many websites that offer the same service, however, so alternatively you can search BMR calculator and find your own.

Before we move on please calculate your BMR and fill in the box below. You can find the calculator here:
http://www.bmi-calculator.net/bmr-calculator/
However, other sources are available.

My Basal Metabolic Rate is ……………… calories

Calculating your target daily energy expenditure (TDEE)

Once you have worked out how many calories your body requires to function and survive daily, we then must take into consideration the extra energy required for daily tasks such as working, walking, and of course training.

Ensuring you have sufficient calories left in the pot after your body has taken out everything it needs for survival is crucial for your performance. We must have spare calories left over to fuel our workouts and to aid in the recovery process.

Your TDEE is another simple equation. It is calculated using your BMR with extra added on dependent on your activity level. Follow the calculator below or search for your own version online. Once you have determined your BMR you will be asked what your activity level is, and you will then be provided with a calculation providing you with an estimated amount of surplus calories to fuel your daily activities.

Before we move on please calculate your TDEE and fill in the box below. You can find the calculator here:
http://www.bmi-calculator.net/bmr-calculator/harris-benedict-equation/
However, other sources are available.

My Target Daily Energy Expenditure is .... calories

What does all this mean for an Irish dancer?

As athletes we always must be sure we are not asking too much of the body, as long term this cannot be sustained and we will break down. Matching your target daily energy expenditure will ensure you are eating enough calories per day to firstly run at optimal health and secondly fuel your performance. It means that you are putting yourself in the best possible position to reach your potential. A diet lacking in calories will provide slower results, increase injury risk, decrease your recovery rate and leave you with less chance of both short-term and long-term success, so it is vital that you are eating sufficient calories every day for optimal health and performance.

Adjusting your calorie intake for weight loss or weight gain

Your target daily energy expenditure will provide you with the amount of calories required to maintain your weight whilst fuelling your performance. This is great if you are already at ideal bodyweight; however, if you are looking for weight loss or weight gain then there is some alteration needed to your TDEE number.

For fat loss we need to be eating less than we are burning off; however, massive calorie drops are not required nor are they healthy and may lead to too much muscle loss. I would start by deducting three hundred calories from your TDEE to give you a calorie deficit. From there monitor your weight and your activity level to see if a larger or smaller deficit is required.

To gain weight we need to be eating more than we are burning off; however, again massive calorie increases are not necessary and may lead to too much body fat gain. I would start by adding three hundred calories to your TDEE number. This will provide you with a decent calorie surplus. From there I would monitor your weight and activity level weekly to see if a larger or smaller calorie surplus is required.

Macronutrient split

Now we know the estimated amount of calories we require each day, what do we actually do with this number? We already know that different foods do different jobs within the body. If my daily calorie requirement is 2,500 per day, how do I know how much protein, carbohydrates and fats I need to make up this number? This is where the macronutrient split comes in.

It would not be a great idea to eat 2,500 calories of carbohydrates each day, with few proteins or fats. Similarly it would not be a good idea to eat 2,500 calories of protein every day and consume no carbohydrates or fats. Therefore we must ensure we balance our food groups to make up the intended amount each day.

The actual ratios of this can vary quite a lot, especially when we consider different goals such as fat loss, muscle gain, athletic performance, etc. Remember a ratio of fifty per cent carbs, thirty per cent protein and twenty per cent fats may only be suitable for someone currently at an ideal bodyweight for optimal performance. We need to remember for those that are not at optimal bodyweight they may need a different caloric intake with varying percentages of food groups. For example, we already know that carbohydrates are not tolerated very well by the overweight population; therefore eating a diet that is fifty per cent carbohydrate-based may be optimal for an athlete, but detrimental for weight loss. As the purpose of this book is athletic development, I will focus purely on teaching you the required amount of each food group for optimal performance.

A ratio of fifty per cent carbohydrates, thirty per cent protein and twenty per cent healthy fats is considered a well-balanced diet. As fifty per cent of your diet is coming from carbohydrates and thirty per cent of your diet coming from protein, this makes it a perfect choice for athletes who require a lot of energy fast and sufficient protein for optimal recovery. These ratios fall within the USDA Dietary Guidelines for Americans 2010. (7)

To work out your overall requirements simply take your number and equate each percentage from it. For example, if my daily calorie requirement was 2,500 calories, after applying the percentage breakdown, the ratios would look like this:

MY CALORIE BREAKDOWN	
My TDEE	2,500 calories
50% Carbohydrates =	1,000 calories
30% Protein =	1,000 calories
20% Fats =	500 calories

Please write your own calorie breakdown in the table provided below:

YOUR CALORIE BREAKDOWN	
Your TDEE	
50% Carbohydrates =	
30% Protein =	
20% Fats =	

Tracking your calories

You are now armed with all the data you need to start using your calorie tracker. Simply choose a well-known calorie tracker application on your phone or computer and start logging everything you eat and drink. At the end of each day you can see how close you were to your daily requirements. This is a great way to hold yourself accountable, help you make healthier food choices, increase recovery and improve performance!

These equations may seem confusing and advanced for most of you; however, I assure you these are very basic calculations that the majority of athletes in professional sports will know and follow to a degree. Knowing this type of information and applying it is the difference between an average athlete and a professional athlete and it will only take several minutes to complete. If you find this in any way confusing or you are unsure how to work this out, please contact me directly and I will personally calculate this for you. Finally, whilst BMR and TDEE are a great way to find your baseline calculations, these are average calculations and individual requirements can vary, depending upon a lot of factors. That said, this is a great starting point for everyone at entry level.

'AS AN ATHLETE YOU DO NOT EAT FOR PLEASURE
– YOU EAT FOR PERFORMANCE.' — Lauren Early

CHAPTER SUMMARY

Important points to note:

- Understand what your Basal Metabolic Rate (BMR) is
- Calculate how many calories are required for your body to survive each day
- Understand what your Target Daily Energy Expenditure (TDEE) is
- Calculate how many calories are required by your body for optimal performance
- Make calorie adjustments for weight loss or weight gain if required
- Practice tracking your calorie intake to hold yourself accountable to your goals

---

Chapter 8
Fuelling your performance

Unfortunately within the health and fitness industry when a person has had success at something such as training or successful weight loss they seem to be granted the power and authority to give advice on the subject to others. If we ask them how it worked they don't understand the human mechanics of the process; they simply followed something that worked and are now giving advice to others. We have all met that person who got great results with a trainer and now appears to have the authority to coach their friends, right?

This, unfortunately, is a big problem. I have coached many athletes and many members of the general public only to find out several months later that they are now giving out advice and helping to coach family members or friends, even though they have zero qualifications within the industry and lack the experience to take the individual needs of that person into consideration. I often remind them that only a few months prior they were seeking coaching advice – do they really believe after such a short period of time they are at the other end of the scale and good enough to give it out? Do not be that person who passes on advice to others based on what has worked for you or your coach.

As a coach, dancer, or parent, careful consideration must be given to our own needs. I cannot stress this enough. There are seven billion humans on earth and no two of us are made exactly the same. When looking at a person's nutrition requirements we must ensure we consider all the fundamental areas that make up that person and their needs, such as genetic make-up, dietary history, current nutritional habits, emotional connections to food, current body composition and, of course, their goals.

Anyone who has received nutrition advice without the above factors being considered is simply following a generic dietary template in the assumption that as it has worked for others, it will also work with them. Whilst it may yield quick results in some cases, most are not sustainable nor do they consider your personal requirements or teach you why the process is working, meaning that once progress halts you don't know what to change or alter to get things going again because you don't know why progress was made in the first place. This naturally leads to you getting fed up and going back to normal eating patterns, resulting in any progress being reversed.

The Internet is the most popular source of information and dietary advice; however, it is probably the worst place we can look for help, simply because the advice offered does not take into consideration any of your individual needs, and most of the information is misleading and conflicting, leaving you even more confused than when you first started reading.

Let's take, for example, milk and dairy products. You are feeling bloated and go online and read an article by someone who recommends that you cut out milk and lactose from your diet.

You immediately stop consuming milk and your bloating reduces. Naturally you begin to tell everyone how bad milk is for you and that they should stop drinking it too, right? So what about those who can tolerate milk and lactose perfectly? They then start to believe your advice and avoid milk.

If someone who can tolerate milk avoids it for a period of time, they will then become intolerant to it. Why? Because if we eliminate a food group our body will stop producing the enzymes responsible for breaking it down, therefore when we put the food – in this case milk – back into our diet, we no longer have the enzymes present to digest it. So through believing the myth that milk is bad for us all, you have taken someone who is not intolerant to milk and essentially made them intolerant to it, all due to your need to pass on advice that you are not qualified to give.

Moving forward, we need to understand we are all different in our requirements and know exactly what we want to achieve from our food. Once we have been honest in our assessment then we can begin to match our goals to the best foods that will help us achieve this in the safest and healthiest way possible. I want you to write your goals in the lines below. As you go through this chapter I want you to constantly remind yourself of your aims and what you need to get out of this. You can do it for yourself, your child or your dancer.

What is the goal I wish to achieve?

....

....

(Examples include: improved competition placing, fat loss, strength, etc.)

What do I need to get from my nutrition?

....

....

(Examples include: more energy, faster recovery, improved performance, etc.)

I will assume you have all purchased this book with the same goal in mind – improving your dance performance. Although the book is aimed at eating for athletic development if, for example, you are a parent or teacher who would like their own nutritional help, then ensure you try to relate all the content to your own goals as you go.

Understanding the difference between a generic diet plan and a true nutritional programme is what will define your successes in your sport, your general health, and your quality of life.

Current standard of nutritional practices in Irish dancing

Fuelling your training and exercise is one of the most important factors in determining your performance and results. However, it is also one of the most overlooked aspects in amateur sports, especially Irish dancing. As a coach in multiple different sports, when I first started coaching in Irish dancing I wrongly assumed that nutrition already played a role in each school and each dancer's training regime. To my amazement, for the majority of dancers it was completely overlooked.

Eating right for optimal athletic performance

Throughout this chapter I want you to think of your body like the engine of a Formula One car. The F1 car is the most complex machine and has the best performing engine on earth! It's well oiled, fully serviced, has a full tank of gas, and is made from the lightest available parts, creating the fastest and sharpest performance and giving the best results possible.

Now let's put that F1 car beside a big heavy truck that's been running on low fuel and has been poorly maintained, always driving and burning out and not getting anywhere near the best performance possible. It's quite easy to see which of the two would win a race.

This scenario is exactly like the human body. As an athlete, just like the F1 car we aim to be lean, fast, sharp and highly tuned, well recovered and well-fuelled, ready to perform at our best in each session.

So where do we start? Let's firstly look at the benefits a properly planned nutrition regime will give us.

A proper nutrition regime will give the following **performance** benefits:

1. Decreased tiredness and fatigue
2. Enhanced concentration and alertness
3. Improved reaction times and speeds
4. Reduced chance of injury
5. Improved recovery rate
6. Allows you to train at a higher intensity output and maintain this for longer
7. Improved body composition – lowered body fat levels and increased muscle mass and strength
8. Improved speed, power and height output
9. Improved immune system and stress hormonal balance

And, of course, all the health benefits that come with clean eating, such as reduced inflammation and reduced cardiac diseases.

(In a second edition I may go into more detail around the general health benefits of food choices; however, for the first edition I will focus

solely on the benefits of nutrition for performance.)

Now we know the benefits that nutrition can bring, what effect do poor nutritional habits have on **performance**?

The effect of poor nutrition on performance

We all know optimal athletic performance pushes our bodies to the edge. If we look at the amount of stress a competitive sport puts on the body along with a poorly controlled diet it is easy to see how injuries or over-training occur. Poor nutrition will eventually put a limit on performance and halt all progression. There comes a point where the body simply cannot progress any further, unless it faces a new stimulus which it is forced to adapt to. Let's say we increase the intensity or the frequency we train; the body will try to adapt to that new stimulus by improving ability, recovery and fatigue so that it can comfortably control and continue at the new intensity or increased frequency.

However, when we are at a top level in sport our body has gone through this adaptation process many times to get us to the level we are currently at, so to improve further we must make sure we have everything in control to support the increased intensity of training. Failing to have adequate nutritional support daily will mean that our bodies will struggle to adapt to the increased intensity of training that we are now putting it through. This will lead to increased fatigue and poor recovery, meaning we may not be recovered in time for our next training session, which will again increase fatigue and slow recovery until eventually the body will stop, either through injury or burnout. What started as a way of bringing your performance to a new level now leaves you tired, injured or stressed, with a lower level of performance.

We can't expect to repeatedly improve performance and recovery efficiently without any other fundamentals changing. Each time we change our training programmes to improve performance and make the intensity that little bit harder we must also ensure we make the correct nutritional improvements and lifestyle adjustments required to support those changes, fuel the new workouts and promote fast and efficient recovery, so that we are ready and fuelled up for our next training session. Failure to do so will result in more effort and harder training, but equal poor results and very little improvement. Much of this failure to improve is generally put down to a poor training programme, before the lifestyle or nutrition habits of the athlete are considered.

We can only establish how good a training programme is if we have our nutrition on point and lead a lifestyle that supports our goals.

Now back to stress. We know continually trying to train harder will raise stress levels in the body. Each time we train we put our body into a state of acute *(short-term)* stress. When we finish our body will try to adapt to the new stimulus so that the next time we train the body will not be under the same duress nor require the same exertion levels to complete the job, meaning the stress will be less than that of the previous session. This is an ideal scenario for the body and the main reason why we improve, so we simply avoid future stresses on the body.

With poor nutrition and poor recovery from one training session to the next, this short-term stress ends up lasting a lot longer after our training and potentially leading into the next session, as our recovery rate is hampered by the lack of nutrients. We have now put too much demand on our body (output) for what we can safely tolerate and recover from and we place our body in a state of chronic stress. This chronic stress derives simply from too much stress *(output)* and not enough recovery or the correct calories to support the recovery process *(input)*. Athletes who tend to have long-term elevated stress levels will usually burn out and eventually get injured. If they are lucky enough to escape injury, usually poor performances and high stress levels are enough to see the athlete leave the sport. Without considering the athlete's lifestyle or dietary habits, most will put this scenario down to the athlete being overtrained.

Overtrained or under-recovered?

Let's imagine for a second that there is no such thing as overtraining and that the athlete can actually only be under-recovered. Both give the same end result but are very different in nature. Of course there is an actual possibility of overtraining, but the reality of this happening is very small. To put this into perspective, I have seen Olympic level athletes train two or three times per day for four years leading up to an Olympic games and never experience an injury or a burnout. Why? Because they have properly controlled training programmes that provide periods of intense training followed by scheduled rest periods. The athletes' nutrition programmes are designed to support their training commitments. They also lead the lifestyle of a professional athlete, their weekends and social life are scheduled around their training goals, not the other way round.

On the other hand I have seen amateur athletes, including many dancers, who train only two to four times per week and yet constantly get injured and never seem to improve. They feel exhausted after a relatively easy session. Their nutrition habits are extremely poor and their recovery time is equally as poor. They have badly designed training programmes promoting too much training stress and too few recovery periods. This athlete will generally have a busy social life, containing late nights, early starts and too little sleep. They generally are not prepared to trade off certain things in their lifestyle to improve performance, but seek to include everything, which we know long term is a recipe for disaster. Burning the candle at both ends!

See the difference?

Overtraining is not detrimental if we use it strategically. The best coaches in the world use overtraining as a method of progression when the athlete goes through a plateau in performance. Quite often a period of overtraining is a great way to shock the body into higher levels of performance – have a period of training hard followed by a rest period and you will almost certainly bounce back stronger!

It is quite easy for someone to put the experience of injury or fatigue down to overtraining. It's human nature to always need someone or something to blame, right?

As a coach or teacher we need to take time to assess our athlete's lifestyle habits outside of training to identify any periods or patterns of under-recovery.

In my experience, having completed hundreds of lifestyle assessments, I usually find that a lack of sleep, poor nutrition, hydration, alcohol and a busy social life have all affected the athlete's ability to recover efficiently going into the next session. From there we elevate the stress levels more and demand more from the body.

An important lesson for all coaches and teachers is that **training can only be as hard as the athlete's lifestyle can support.** Of course not all athletes will be honest in this assessment, but it is important to make them aware that their performance will suffer if everything around them outside of training isn't in place.

Those who aren't willing to be compliant need to be made aware that in this instance the lack of performance isn't the fault of the coach or teacher – it is that of the athlete and their unwillingness to trade off certain pleasures for an improvement in performance.

Trade-offs, sacrifices and lifestyle changes

The one thing that always stands out when I first consult with a new client or athlete is their need to tell me they won't be happy until they reach a certain goal. I have come across people who have told me they won't be happy until they get abs, others have told me they won't be happy until they win a certain competition. The problem with this is if I then tell you it will take me a year to get you those abs or get you in the right condition to win that competition it means you are saying you won't be happy for a year. And guess what? Once you get those abs or win that competition, if you want to continue to have your abs showing or to compete at that level you are going to have to continue to do everything you did over the last year that got you there. See the problem?

You must enjoy the process of getting you to your goal, otherwise when you get there you will be left miserable knowing you now have to continue doing the same things that got you there in the first place, and if you didn't enjoy the process then what are the chances that you will continue?

Another point to mention is that many people will set timeframes on certain goals. As athletes this can be great; however, one slight problem with setting a timeframe is that you tell yourself all the sacrifices you have to make between now and then are only temporary to get you to where you need to be. Let's go back to the same examples above. In twelve weeks' time I want to have visible abs, or in twelve weeks' time I want to win this competition. Over the next twelve weeks you will restrict certain foods, clamp down on your social life, and weekends will be almost non-existent. These are sacrifices to get you to where you want to be. Throughout this period you will want to go out with friends and you will want to eat bad foods, but you will remind yourself of the amount of weeks you have left to go, meaning that when this time period is over you will want to eat everything in sight and return to your normal lifestyle, indulging in everything you gave up and more.

To continue with what you have achieved you must follow the lifestyle that got you there in the first place. If you restrict certain foods to get you those summer abs, what do you think happens when the twelve weeks are over? And if you win that competition by having no social life and training twice per day to get you into top condition, what happens when the competition is over?

We must understand that it is not sacrifices but lifestyle changes that we need to make. Some can change more than others long term, so we need to be sensible in our approach to achieving our goals; what you are doing to achieve them will need to be continued afterwards.

Try to live a balanced lifestyle. You can go out with friends and socialise at the weekends and still stay on track towards your goals. Ultimately if your friends are true friends they will help you through it and support you, as opposed to tempting you with bad foods.

Dining out

Before placing your order think about how you would order after the meal has finished. If you had to order again, would you order something different given a second chance? A menu will always be packed with food that you want to order; after all, a menu is created to make the foods sound delicious. Ask yourself, 'What should I order?' and 'What do I want to order?' If they are two different things go with what you should order. Your body and performance will thank you for it.

FOR THE DANCER

How to establish your own nutritional requirements

Analysing your current nutrition regime

Before I teach you how to make the necessary changes to improve your performance and quality of life, I first want you to analyse and break down your existing diet. In order to know where we need to go, we must first know where we are coming from.

The first thing I want you to do is write everything down that you have consumed today. If you don't feel like today has been a particularly good day or similar to what it normally would be, write down a typical day instead. Please include all liquids and supplementation.

Now that you have your daily food diary in front of you I want you to look over it. Many people don't realise how poor or inconsistent their nutrition actually is until they note it down. Keep scanning through and get a clear overview of everything that has gone in.

Now that you have had a chance to analyse your diet based on what you have just written, I am going to ask you, how would you rate your current diet? Please circle below the answer that most reflects your current level of nutrition.

POOR   **AVERAGE**   **PERFECT**

Without seeing your book I can pretty much guess that most readers have circled poor or average, right?

Let's think about this for a second. I have asked you to rate your own diet and you tell me it is poor or average. We cannot say something is poor or average if we do not have something to compare it to, i.e. we must know what perfect looks like in order to label our own as poor or average. In other words, by saying it's average you are acknowledging that you already know what is wrong with it, otherwise you would be circling that it is perfect, right?

The real truth is that most of us already know what is wrong with our nutrition to a certain degree. We tend to know a lot more than we realise about the subject and we just want someone with authority to confirm it to us or take control of the situation to make the changes.

The difference between the general public and an athlete is that successful athletes have self-control, whereas the general public does not. I want you to take control and go back to your food diary. Note down everything that you think is wrong with it. It may be too much sugar, too many soft drinks, not enough protein, not enough food or water – whatever you think is wrong or could be made better, note it down.

Things to look out for:

1. How many meals have a protein source included *(animal protein)?*
2. How many meals have vegetables / fibre?
3. How much water is included in the day?
4. Which meals have sugar?
5. Which meals have healthy carbohydrates?
6. How frequent are the meals – what is the time lapse between them?

Now you are armed with all this information you will see that you have the power and knowledge to make the necessary changes and take the first step to improving your nutrition.

DO IT!!!!

I have completed this exercise with countless athletes in the past, especially those that are at beginner level or too young to follow exact nutrition programmes. It is an excellent way for the athlete to take control and apply their own knowledge into their training. For a parent or teacher, this is a great task to complete with your child or dancer. Sit down with them and allow them to honestly assess their nutrition, then have them write down which areas they could improve on. This will be the first step towards improving performance and living a healthier lifestyle.

Designing your own food plate

Up to this point you have learnt what all the food groups are and what their roles are within the body. You have also dissected your own daily nutrition regime and noted any issues, identifying what is wrong and what changes you would make. In this final section we are going to design a food plate from scratch, together. Below I have outlined the basic principles that as an athlete you can adopt into your own daily nutrition regimes to improve performance and enhance the recovery process.

Grab an empty plate and let's design your meal from scratch!

Step 1 – Protein as a baseline ingredient with every meal

When planning our daily meals it is most important that we spread protein out across the day. We know from what we learnt in chapter 4 that protein cannot be stored, therefore it's important to add it in small amounts to every meal for ongoing absorption. Choose your source of animal protein, add it to your plate, and let's go to Step 2.

Step 2 – Vegetables and fibre with every meal

Now that we have our main source of protein, we need to add some fibre to help with the digestion of the meal. A portion of green and coloured vegetables will provide you with the fibre you require, not to mention the vitamins and minerals they also provide!

Step 3 – Choose your energy source for the meal

As athletes we need to be fuelled up! Step 3 is where you choose your gas for your engine! With the exception of after exercise we would look to add in a source of slow release energy to keep us going throughout the day. Choose your source of starchy carbohydrates, such as oatmeal, yams or grains to finish off your food plate!

Step 4 – Add simple sugars post exercise

In the post training window of around thirty minutes your body is like a sponge ready to soak up all essential nutrients to replenish your gas tank and kick start the recovery process! This is the golden window for all you sugar junkies to be able to eat sugar successfully and it will actually benefit the body! This is a great time to switch your starchy carbohydrates for some fruits and simple sugars.

Step 5 – Include healthy fats throughout the day

Do not overlook the healthy fats *(not all fats are bad, as explained earlier in chapter 6)*. Healthy unsaturated fats such as extra virgin olive oil, avocado, eggs and nuts provide the body with essential nutrients, better brain function, improved mood and enhanced focus. All great for mental preparation for the athlete!

Step 6 – Hydration

A dehydrated muscle will not perform at its best nor be at its strongest! A hydrated muscle will be full of energy, fired up and ready to work. Ensure you drink three to four litres of water daily. If you find this difficult, try having a large glass of water with every meal, spread across the day.

Step 7 – Supplement

We already know how hard it is to get all of our required vitamins and minerals through the food we eat. It requires strict planning and more often than not life will get in the way of maintaining a perfect diet. Daily supplementation ensures you are covering the chances of any deficiencies, giving your health and performance the best chance possible! Read the nutrition section below and include basic supplementation as part of your morning regime.

Step 8 – Sleep

You can have the best diet in the world, but if you don't get enough sleep at night you will almost certainly decrease your performance and health. Lack of sleep will raise your stress levels, put more pressure on your body and wreak havoc with your digestive system. Do not burn the candle at both ends!

Sleep is where we grow, where we gain strength and where our performance improves. Get to bed early and wake up refreshed and ready for another day of working towards your goals.

You should seek professional advice from a dietician when looking for a personalised food plan. The steps I have given below are basic ways of making small changes for the better in your diet. This is not meant to advise you to create your own nutrition plan, it is merely guidance that you, your coach or parent can follow to ensure you are getting sufficient foods and the right quality of foods each day.

FOR THE TEACHER

How to establish the nutritional and lifestyle requirements of your dancers for optimal performance

Coaching support for the athlete's lifestyle and nutritional requirements

We have covered the basic principles for an athlete to create their own nutrition plan; however, not all athletes will have the self-control to implement such changes alone. As a dance coach it is not your role to act as a nutritionist or dietician; however, there are several things you can do to highlight the importance of quality nutrition and the need to lead a lifestyle that will support the intensity of a dancer's training. By simply highlighting these areas you will hold the athlete that little bit more accountable and increase their self-control and compliance.

As a coach I recommend you spend individual time with your athlete and get to know their lifestyle choices outside of dance class. At the beginning of each season, after a hard earned break, sit down with the dancer and discuss the dancer's goals for the year ahead. Once both the athlete and the coach have decided on the goals for the year, take time to assess the following areas. You need to know your athlete better than they know themselves so that you can give an honest assessment as to whether their goals are attainable, given their lifestyle outside of class.

Step 1 – Complete a lifestyle questionnaire

Providing your dancer with a lifestyle questionnaire shows that you require one hundred per cent compliance, both inside and outside of class, and that you are interested in their life away from the studio. This will give the dancer confidence in you as a coach and your ability to take them to the top.

A good lifestyle questionnaire should cover all areas such as sleep, social life, work or school commitments, free time, hobbies, daily energy levels, stress levels, alcohol consumption, smoker / non-smoker, etc. and leave you with a clear picture of the athlete's life outside of class. You can then review how their lifestyle fits the given training goals for the year and discuss any potential trade-offs and changes that need to be made to support the new training goals.

I have attached a sample lifestyle questionnaire in chapter 10 that you can adopt and use with your athletes.

Step 2 – Establish the athlete's compliance

Task the dancer to create a daily food log over the course of a week; this will show several things.

Firstly it will allow you as a coach to determine how much food is being consumed each day, the quality of foods being eaten and the state of hydration the athlete is in each day. This can then be compared with their strength and performance levels, recovery ability, body fat percentage and current / past injuries to determine how their existing nutrition is supporting their lifestyle.

Secondly, giving your dancer a task to complete for you outside of class will show you how compliant that dancer is or will be in the future. If they go home and spend the next few days logging all of their food and water intake and present this back to you, it shows that they are willing to complete tasks outside of dance class and proves their dedication. This bodes well for when they are tasked with sprint or strength sessions to be completed individually, as we now know there is a high chance the athlete will complete all training as planned. If the athlete fails to return a food log or rushes to bring in a half-completed log, then we know they are likely also to give less or no commitment to the extra training that must be completed outside of class.

Step 3 – Let the athlete make the initial changes

Above I outlined the benefits of having the dancer make the initial changes to their nutrition, and the same can be done for their lifestyle. After completing a lifestyle questionnaire ask the dancer whether they feel their current lifestyle reflects that of the goals just given. From this have the dancer make the initial changes of were improvements could be made. Examples would be more sleep, less social media, more practice, etc.

Step 4 – Establish the athlete's body type

Nutrition is part of an athlete's long-term success; however, alone it is a poor predictor of performance. There are many other factors we must consider when determining the fundamentals of great performance, such as energy levels, strength levels, dance performance, current body fat percentage and lifestyle habits.

It is never a good idea to solely use one measurement tool to assess an athlete. We must use all the measurement tools available and we can then compare results against each other for a clearer picture of what is going on overall.

For example, it is not enough to check someone's food log and make assumptions before comparing this list of foods against their lifestyle questionnaire, then comparing their lifestyle choices against their current bodyweight and performance level. We need to know what condition that food log and the lifestyle they live has got them into. Checking if their body fat is ascending weight or descending weight, and whether their performance is improving or declining, will give us a clearer picture of how these fundamental areas are affecting the body. We can also look at injures and recovery rates, then put together a whole overview based on all the measurement tools, and not just one.

Anyone can look at a food log and determine the calories are too high or too low. Anyone can also look at someone's lifestyle and determine there are too many late nights and too little training being done, but we cannot assume this without looking at the effect it is having on the body and performance. Remember, everyone is different. Some can handle less sleep and later nights, whereas others of us simply can't. Do not make immediate assumptions based on a food log and a lifestyle questionnaire without comparing this against the athlete's weight and performance. Once you have all the necessary answers and tools ask yourself, based on all of this information is the dancer's weight in an increasing or decreasing trend? And is their performance improving or declining? Based on these answers you can help the athlete and parents make the necessary changes.

Step 5 – Ensure the athlete is at his / her optimal competition weight

As coaches, our job is to ensure our athletes are at their optimal performance come competition time, right? Part of achieving that is making sure the athlete is at their optimal bodyweight for the competition. Allowing a dancer to compete above ideal competition weight not only reduces the dancer's chances of success, but we are forcing them to work twice as hard on stage, increasing the amount of pressure going through the joints and thus increasing the risk of injury. At the same time as coaches we expect them to move just as fast, be as powerful and generate the same amount of lift as do the competition. Agreed, it can be a complex conversation to have with an athlete, especially the younger and less dedicated they are, however as coaches we must recognise that it is unfair to the athlete to be put in the position of competing whilst being disadvantaged, and the dancer and parent should respect this. *(See chapter 3 for all the benefits of optimal power to weight ratio.)*

Step 6 – Educate your dancer

As a dance teacher it is important to highlight the benefits that strength training, nutrition and hydration can bring to the dancer's performance. Each athlete must know and understand the recovery process and food groups so they can make better, informed choices. Most other sports teams will hire an external strength coach and nutritionist to give a talk to their dancers about the benefits both these areas can bring. This is something dancing as a sport is not familiar with and hopefully a as a teacher reading this book you now have enough information to educate your dancers. If you do not feel comfortable, I recommend having each dancer read this handbook as an entry requirement into your school. This will set a standard of entrance and make your school more desirable. Setting the standards early will lead to improved discipline and will mean everyone will be on the same page, having all read and understood the content in this book as part of the joining process. If the dancer is a beginner have the parents read a copy of this book to outline the standards that you expect and ultimately show that you are serious about what you do. It is most important to lay out your expectations early. Ultimately, as a coach or dance teacher you are hired to produce results, and whilst some may see this as extreme they will thank you when the dancer is on stage performing at their best.

Step 7 – Ongoing adjustments

Everyone's lifestyle and nutrition will change on an ongoing basis. I recommend assessing the athlete at least once per year. The more professional the athlete, the more frequent the assessment. The reason for frequent assessments is so that you can make continual adjustments to their training and lifestyle. It allows you to adjust according to training intensity, frequency, volume, discuss training performance, check body fat percentage etc., so that you are helping keep the dancer compliant throughout the year. Otherwise, based on annual assessments, if compliance isn't monitored throughout the year athletes tend to slowly drift back into their usual patterns.

FOR THE PARENT

Nutrition and supplementation for the younger athlete

Everyone should be given the right to eat a well-balanced, healthy diet, especially children. The first thing we need to realise is that younger athletes generally aren't in control of what they eat. As food is provided to them by their parents, they will naturally follow the same dietary patterns of their family. This presents two immediate problems.

1. Parents have reached full development and growth.
2. In most cases the parents are not undertaking as much physical activity as the child.

As the younger athlete is still in the growth phase of life, they must eat a diet that provides them with all the key nutrients for full growth and development. On top of this they must also eat for the additional energy requirement of their sport to support the higher level of activity. We can see how development and recovery can be compromised if nutritional requirements are not considered. Firstly we must establish a healthy eating pattern, regardless of the sport, to ensure we give our children the best health possible. Eating for performance should be an extension of eating for a healthy lifestyle; we should not eat a healthy diet just because we are involved in a sport.

Whilst supplementation is not a necessity we must ensure that the athlete / child is not depleted or deficient in any important vitamins or minerals. Many parents will avoid supplements for children, thinking that they will get all their requirements through foods. That can be true if you have a one hundred per cent perfect diet, but unfortunately this is never usually the case. The truth is very rarely will we see any athlete that gets all their requirements through foods. We only have to look at the school cafeteria menu to see how poor the quality of foods are that the children are consuming.

Another big debate we tend to hear is the use of whey protein shakes in younger athletes. It seems to be a common theory that not only can they weight train after they reach sixteen years of age, but they can also have protein shakes at this magical age. Does our digestive system automatically change on our sixteenth birthday?

It is not a necessity for anyone to supplement with protein powder as long as we are getting sufficient protein intake in our diet, but yet again most diets are made up with very little protein *(or very little of anything beneficial)* meaning the recovery and growth rate of the child will be impaired.

Whey protein is not some magical supplement – it is a product of milk protein in powdered form – so if you allow your child milk it is essentially the same as allowing a protein supplement. It is exactly like eating protein in its whole form, only it is more digestible, making it a perfect choice to kick start the recovery process if taken directly after a workout.

The general rule for usage is if you are not sensitive to lactose / whey it is completely safe to supplement with a powered protein regardless of your age. If you have any allergies, digestive problems or do not tolerate milk very well avoid protein-based powder and opt for whole food sources of protein instead. Either way, get enough protein!

Reward foods / punishment foods

The most important rule with nutrition for the younger athlete is that we do not develop any poor relationships with food that will potentially stay with the child for life. We hear so often that one day carbs are bad, the next day fat is bad, the next day sugar is bad and the conflicting information will go on and on.

The truth is, there is no such thing as bad foods given they are used at the right time and with the right person. For example, while sugars may be bad for someone who is overweight and not involved in much activity, it is the perfect fuel for an athlete to use during workout or post workout to replenish those glycogen stores. That's why it's not necessarily about the foods themselves, but more about when they are being used and who is using them.

With the younger athlete we need to ensure a broad diet including a range of foods that change frequently so that the child does not get into the habit of thinking certain foods are bad and certain foods are good. I recently have seen an influx in coaches prescribing food plans for younger athletes and I myself have had a surge of requests for these. Food plans limit the child to a certain group of foods and a certain amount of calories. What is needed is a reference guide to help children and parents in making better food choices without actually enforcing strict rules regarding what foods should be eaten and in what exact amounts. Foods plans do not educate the athlete or parent on the reasons why these foods are included, they merely know they need to eat what's on the list. However, without learning the reasoning behind this the parent / athlete can never learn or adapt the plan, they either follow it or break it. It is much more important for the parent / athlete to learn which foods do what within the body so that they can then make their own informed choices early on.

Enforcing strict plans with no allowance for variance is how we will build up bad relationships with foods. What do you think happens when the child gets a break from their food plan? They are going to indulge in all the foods they weren't allowed – more than ever before. Why is this? Because all the foods that have been restricted for so long now become seen as a reward for sticking to a plan, therefore they will more than likely over indulge more than they would if they were freely allowed these foods at any time. We always want what we can't have, right?

Another problem I see is parents labelling foods as reward foods for their child, i.e. the child will get a treat if they do something good. Whilst I am all for giving out rewards for their successes and achievement and teaching good behavioural habits, should that reward really be food?

Let's think about what happens when we give a child a 'reward' food. They indulge and get short-term pleasure from the food. But then, when the child resumes normal eating patterns of protein based meals and vegetables, they will automatically see these bland foods as 'punishment' foods. Always remember the rule of reverse psychology – giving someone a reward food automatically means that the reverse is also true – 'daily foods that aren't rewards all of a sudden are seen as a punishment and the desire for these reward foods become greater because of the restriction placed on them.

Try to avoid this by including such 'reward' foods in small amounts each day at strategic times, without actually labelling them as a reward. A good start would be to place sugar-based foods post workout. Not only will they replenish glycogen stores, but the child freely consumes them, without any restriction or label placed on them, meaning their desire for them will be less as they know they can have them frequently. Reward the child for their hard work with other treats, such as cinema tickets, presents or new sports clothing.

My top nutrition tips for the younger athlete

1. Eat enough for growth and development

As discussed, the primary goal with any child is that they have sufficient food and the right types of foods in their diet to ensure optimal bone growth and development. They will not get this from your regular school cafeteria, so ensure you adapt their diet accordingly. Health comes first, regardless of sporting performance.

2. Eat extra calories to fuel workouts and recovery

Once we have covered the importance of food for development, we now need to ensure we provide the body with extra energy to fuel the workouts and extra protein to aid in optimal recovery. Without this the body will tap into the daily calories we need for growth and development *(shown above)* resulting in a lack of calories for growth or recovery – or both!

3. Eat enough protein daily

One of the most overlooked aspects of the younger athlete's

nutrition programme is the level of protein intake. Children will generally be well fuelled from all the sugary foods consumed, but one thing you can usually guarantee is that there will almost always be a shortfall in their daily protein intake. Remember protein cannot be stored for use throughout the day *(see protein section in chapter 4)* so this leads to the requirement of small feedings of protein with each meal throughout the day. One portion of meat with dinner or one small slice of ham surrounded in bread is simply not enough across a twenty-four hour period, we need recovery to happen round the clock. Get on top of your protein intake!

4. Drink enough water

Children are so active that it is extremely hard for them to stay hydrated and keep electrolyte levels controlled and this, coupled with the fact that they see water as boring and would rather have sugary based juices, tends to lead to the higher levels of dehydration that we commonly see with younger athletes. It is hard for them to understand the importance of staying hydrated throughout the day and take extra quantities of water around training. How many times has your child come out of class with a water bottle still full?

Try to add some freshly squeezed lemon or lime juice to their water, as not only will it flavour the water and make it more enjoyable, but it will also help keep their body alkaline, which is important for athletes that compete in a lactic acid based sport such as Irish dancing. If you are feeling extra dedicated, add a pinch of coloured salt to the water; this adds additional electrolytes and helps replace those lost during exercise and sweating. It makes the perfect hydration drink to use throughout the day, without all the sugar of a sports drink.

5. Supplement where necessary

A smart athlete will realise how hard it is to get all their requirements from foods and will include basic supplementation to ensure all the boxes are ticked and leave no room for poor performance or potential deficiencies. Basic supplementation *(such as those shown in chapter 4)* are all natural supplements required by the body, therefore are completely safe given the child has no allergies. Again, whey protein is also completely safe and should be used where protein intake isn't sufficient or the athlete's schedule does not allow for frequent feedings, which can lead to a deficit of protein.

6. Do not stick to strict food plans

Avoid neglecting certain food groups and do not adopt a strict rule of implementing dietary plans at such a young age, as there is a risk associated with the effect teaching such strict regimens so early in life may have, especially when they cannot be maintained forever. If the athlete begins to reach high levels of performance later in life it is possible to move on to a tailored nutritional plan. In the meantime, leave room for improvement and adaptation when necessary. Instead get educated on making healthier food choices based around improving overall health, improving performance and ensuring optimal recovery. Not only will that information benefit the child but, once learned, it will often be adopted into the family's nutritional regime also.

7. Eat a broad range of foods

Eating a broad range of foods means we get the full benefits of what foods have to offer. Including a variety of fruits and vegetables is a great way to introduce the child to different foods and colours on the plate. No one wants to eat the same foods day after day, especially not a child. Giving variety means the child sees something different on the plate each day. Alternate different colours of fruits and vegetables, different meat sources and different carbohydrate sources, leading to a balanced diet including all food groups and keeping the child interested the whole way through. Time to ditch the turkey dinosaurs and smiley potato faces – these will offer very little in the way of nutritional benefits!

8. Avoid creating bad relationships with foods

Do not place a 'reward' label on certain foods. Avoiding reward foods will stop the child seeing normal daily foods as a punishment. Instead try to reward with different things and keep foods all equal, strategically placing higher calorie or sugary foods around training and at the same time educating the child as to the great benefits each meal brings to their athletic performance.

'WHEN ORDERING FOOD, THINK ABOUT HOW YOU WOULD ORDER AFTER THE MEAL HAS FINISHED; IF YOU HAD TO ORDER AGAIN WOULD YOU CHOOSE SOMETHING DIFFERENT? — Lauren Early

---

CHAPTER SUMMARY

Important points to note:

- Ensure all your individual needs are considered before creating a nutrition plan
- Training can only be as hard as the athlete's lifestyle can support
- Enjoy the process of achieving your goals, otherwise you will not be happy once you get there
- Create your own food diary and start by changing what you already know is wrong with it
- Complete a questionnaire with each of your dancers to learn about their life choices outside of dance class
- When dealing with nutrition for children ensure they have extra calories for growth and development on top of their training commitments

PART 4

PUTTING IT ALL TOGETHER

Now that you know the person you are, the training you need to do and the foods you should be eating. I will now leave you back in the hands of Lauren as she puts the final pieces together to teach you the best ways to prepare for a major championship.

For the first time ever Lauren is about to share with you her top tips and secrets from her extensive experience in competition preparation.

Keep focused and let's put it all together!

Overview

Thus far you have all taken in a lot of information, most of which will be completely new to you and some of which you still might not grasp or fully understand until later in your career, and that is OK. This book is designed for dancers, teachers and parents at all levels and ages. Whilst I know there will be sections that many may need to read again, there will also be many sections that you have learnt a lot from already. My desire is that collectively as a family, school or sport, you can all take something away from the book so that you can share it with others who may have understood a different part than you. We can help each other learn, motivate one other and continue to build progress and improve the sport of Irish dancing forever!

You have learnt a lot of information throughout this book and now that it is coming to an end you may be wondering where to start. Everything in this book plays an important role in progressing your performance; however, there are certain things that will improve your performance faster than others.

I want to leave you with a clear understanding of how to put everything together and get started, and the information in the next chapters will do just that.

In Chapter 9 I will teach you how to best prepare for a major competition once all the hard training and practise has been done.

In Chapter 10 I will give you my final ten commandments. These are my top ten rules, which you must adopt straight away for an immediate change in your performance.

At the back of the book I have provided you with a 'Useful information' section. This section gathers together all the training programmes, nutrition programmes and fitness test tables that you have seen throughout the book, so that in the future you only have to go to the one place to find all of your training information. Every training programme is backed up with videos found online to help support your ongoing training and help you perfect your technique.

The hard work has been done; are you ready to put it all together with me?

Chapter 9
Preparing for a major

Looking the part

To look the part you must dress the part. There will be some who argue that the finer details such as socks, make-up and how you walk on are irrelevant and that the outcome is determined simply by how you dance. Whether this is true or not, always remember the mentality that being prepared will bring. Simply going through detailed preparation will automatically make you a more confident dancer as you will know beyond doubt you have everything covered. Knowing you have done everything from your very first off season training session right down to checking the detail of your stage socks will give you an advantage over everyone else, who in the final stages will begin to doubt their ability due to lack of preparation. I will ensure you leave nothing to chance.

Females – Make sure you have completed your dress rehearsals weeks before your competition day, as well as a tan and make-up trial, so nothing goes wrong or looks out of place on your big day. You have to remember you are dancing on a stage that will have very strong lights, so you need to ensure your make-up and tan are planned for stage lighting and not natural light.

You need to look outstanding. Your dresses need to fit like a glove and sit at the right length on your leg. I recommend having the dress length starting at three inches above the knee. Do not hide your lower quadricep muscle, which is situated just above the knee. This is your most powerful muscle and allowing the judges to watch it produce your power across the stage will display your athleticism.

Please ensure your legs are nicely tanned and try to match your tan to the colour of the make-up on your face. Ensure the colours combine to make you look more natural. Also, remember leg colour cannot be too light or too dark. Please do not forget about the back of your neck, as when you do elevated moves your wig lifts up and we can see it. Also, have a bun wig in where your neck is visible throughout. For tanning, if you have really pale skin I recommend you either put on tanning wipes two days before your competition or get a spray tan on your whole body. Once you have a base colour built up, when you apply your make-up on competition day it will develop a perfect natural looking tone and you will avoid the last minute orange colour that we have all seen.

Girls, please remember your socks need to be crystal white for every single round. I recommend putting on a new pair for each round of competition to avoid stains and unwanted tan marks from the previous rounds. Please wear your socks at a good length to suit your leg shape, i.e. your calf and quadricep muscles. If you have a bigger calf, it's always nice to put your socks under the thickness of the muscle as it will let the judge see your calf work while you dance, another great way to show your athleticism and power. If your genetics mean you have no detail or shape in your calf, with the same thickness of muscle from knee to ankle, I recommend wearing your socks a little higher, up to the top of the calf. The thickness of the sock will help give your legs an improved muscular shape.

Each year in the weeks leading up to a major, I would save up my weekly pocket money so that I could go and buy something nice. Whether it was a sports top or shorts or trainers, I always made sure I had something new to wear on the day I danced at a major championship. The reason for this is purely psychological, when I put the item on in the morning I immediately felt like a million dollars. Feeling good puts you in a positive mood, you see everything in a different light, it makes you take in the special day that's about to begin. When you walk into the competition hall you feel great, you feel confident, you look good, and you know it's time to shine. Dancers, try it out. It does not have to be anything expensive, but please get up and dress to your performance that day! I promise you it will help your mindset and it worked for me every time. Prepare for something physically and you will feel prepared mentally.

Males – You need to make sure your trousers aren't too short, meaning that we can see the bottom half of your legs. Trousers and shirts need to be clean and perfectly ironed. Any rhinestones on your waistcoats or blazers need to be glued to perfection, with ties pinned securely so that they don't pop out when dancing. A good tip is to make sure you use sock glue on your socks, keeping them to your knees. This keeps them secure and in one place, meaning if your trouser leg lifts up we see the black of the sock blending in with your trousers rather than your skin. This will appear much more professional to the judges and won't disrupt the look of your performance. Finally, do not forget about your hairstyle. As a male dancer you do not have many options to stand out; however, you need to maximise the options you do have. A well-groomed hairstyle will look awesome on stage and catch the eye of everyone before you even dance.

Stage presence – what are judges the looking for?

The first chance a judge will get to see you is the moment you walk on that stage. You have approximately five seconds of walking when everyone in the arena is watching you. Judges may not realise it but they are already marking you – not physically, they are marking you mentally by observing everything about you as you walk. If you walk on with a timid approach they expect a timid performance. If you walk on confidently they expect a confident performance and will be more inclined to watch you the whole way through. I personally feel that having a great walk on will buy you attention at least for the first ten to twenty seconds of your performance. A great walk on will draw the judges' attention to you, and once you have that attention you must make sure the first seconds of your dance live up to the expectation you just brought onto that stage. If it does you will steal the attention from the other dancers and all eyes will stay on you, but if your first ten seconds do not live up to your walk on then eyes will start to look elsewhere. Steal the attention from the first step on stage, walk on broadcasting that you are about to give something special, and ensure you follow it through with a great start (and finish) to your performance.

Knowing why we should walk on confidently is one thing, but many do not know how to develop a great walk on. Firstly, let's look at your posture.

Posture

Stand up as tall as possible. Standing tall improves your self-confidence as you feel more dominant. Your shoulder blades must be contracted, and your chin up. Your nose must be in the air with your arms falling perfectly at your sides.

Don't rush your walk and don't make it too slow, either; you need to ensure it is just at the right tempo. A slow walk will suggest fear, as if you don't want to dance. A fast walk will make it look like you are rushing and you just want to get it over with. Walk like you're taking everything in your stride and soaking up the experience!

People used to say I walked on stage like an Alsatian dog

because my nose was in the air, and come to think of it I probably did. I don't know if that's a good thing or a bad thing, but the most important thing is I was remembered for something I did. Being remembered is great because it means you stand out from the rest of the crowd. You should each be remembered for something. Be that girl who is remembered for the big smile or the man who walks on stage with the long stride. Whatever it is, it will define you; look at it like it's your signature, it's your own trademark and will let everyone see who you are. They may not know your name, but if they see you at a competition again they will remember that one thing about you that identifies you. It will keep you in the forefront of people's minds and that in itself can only be a good thing.

When your performance begins make sure you immediately burst into power and take over the stage. Remember to cover all judges and not bump into the other dancers who are on stage with you. You need to know every angle you have to be facing for every single move, own the stage, display your power and acceleration, so that you have your own clear path, forcing the other dancers to move around you.

'STANDING TALL IMPROVES YOUR SELF-CONFIDENCE – ALWAYS STAND TALL.' — Lauren Early

Chapter 10

My ten commandments

My Top Ten Ways to improve your Irish dance performance immediately

Rule No. 1. Improve your lower back strength

Most dancers have extremely weak lower backs. Lower back strength will determine your reaction time and acceleration across the first five metres, which is crucial for a dancer. Remember that your current speed and reaction times are a direct link to your current level of lower back strength!

Rule No. 2. Strengthen your upper body

As Irish dancing is a full body sport, enhancing your upper body strength will make you move faster. To achieve maximal speed the power from the right leg must be counteracted by the torque of the left upper body, therefore you must strengthen your upper body – particularly your upper and lower back – for optimal speed and sharpness without any rotation on top!

Two lots of six week upper body programmes per year are sufficient; it does not need to be year round

Rule No. 3. Reduce your risk of injury

Irish dancing is plagued by injuries! Include structural balance training in the off season, with the focus on strengthening the opposing muscle groups to aid in a better structural balance year round, thus reducing your chances of injury.

Also remember dynamic stretching pre workout, static stretching post workout!

Rule No. 4. Less is more

Too much aerobic work is being completed. Reduce the volume of work, increase the intensity of everything you do, and focus on the expression of power and speed, limiting aerobic work and maximising anaerobic / lactic acid based training.

Rule No. 5. Get strong – lift weights!

Lifting weights will not make you massive – no one ever woke up freakily huge. It doesn't happen by accident and it will not happen overnight. In fact, even most of those who train to look this way find it difficult to achieve naturally. As dancers, we must be as strong as possible to aid in the development of our speed, power and performance. Including regular strength work in your programme will help you reach your optimal level of performance faster, not to mention improve muscle tone, reduce unwanted body fat and create a healthy athletic physique!

Rule No. 6. Eat for performance

Remember as athletes we eat for performance, not for pleasure. Adopt the nutritional strategies you have learnt in this book and fuel your engine!

Rule No. 7. Improve your power to weight ratio

Too many dancers are not at their optimal body fat percentage for competition. Increasing the demands on the body for performance increases injury chances and results in reduced speed, power and acceleration. Ensure clean eating habits in your pre-season training to slash unwanted body fat.

Rule No. 8. Avoid negativity

Surround yourself with positive likeminded people, people who make you feel good about yourself, who keep you on your toes, who are hardworking, happy and goal driven. Find people who are travelling along their own road to success. Avoid the negative people who have zero willpower, they will only bring you down. Maintain focus and achieve your dreams.

Rule No. 9. Be the person everyone wants to be around

Be the person people can't wait to see in their day. Pick people up when others put them down. Talk less and listen more, say hello to everyone, wear a smile, dress to impress, walk with confidence, inspire others and wake up thankful to have another day to work towards your goals! Those who bring happiness into the lives of others cannot keep it from themselves.

Rule No. 10. BE SO GOOD THEY CAN'T IGNORE YOU!

Epilogue

I hope throughout this book we have made you all laugh and cry, touched your heart and helped you dig out that inner desire to be successful, no matter what your goal is in life. I hope as you finish this book you are smiling, feeling positive, and happy, knowing that you CAN and WILL achieve your goals. I hope you will be putting your goals beside your bedside table or up on your wall. On the path to becoming a champion you will meet many new people, share many experiences and develop strong qualities that not only will stay with you forever, but will also develop you as a person to help you in every aspect of your life. The choice to Reach New Heights in your life simply starts with a single decision to do so.

You've read the book, you've found yourself, you've laid out your goals and we have provided you with the path that will take you there, there is only one thing left to do …
Now it's time to start your own journey – are you ready?

Shall we walk it together?

… Let's go!

'YOUR JOURNEY SO FAR IS A REFLECTION OF THE CHOICES YOU HAVE ALREADY MADE. YOUR ACHIEVEMENTS TO COME WILL ONE DAY BE THE REFLECTION OF THE CHOICES YOU ARE ABOUT TO MAKE.' — Lauren Early & Robert McAvoy

'REACHING NEW HEIGHTS'

The End

USEFUL INFORMATION
Training Programmes, Nutrition Plans & Reference Tables

Teachers and coaches

In chapter 4 Robert discussed the importance of, as a teacher, sitting down individually with your dancers at the beginning of each year and the benefits that can bring. The one-to-one meeting would cover the previous year's performance and lay out goals for the coming season. To start off I have provided you with a lifestyle questionnaire (below). This will allow you as a teacher to gain more knowledge about the dancer's lifestyle outside of class and allow you to suggest changes to help support their recovery and dance performance.

IRISH DANCER'S LIFESTYLE QUESTIONNAIRE
(FOR TEACHERS & COACHES)

Date...........................

Lifestyle

Name:
Age:
Do you smoke?
Do you drink alcohol?

How many hours do you sleep on average per night?

Describe your job / school; is it sedentary, active or physically demanding?

On a scale of 0-10, how would you rate your stress levels?

0 - 1 - 2 - 3 - 4 - 5 - 6 - 7 - 8 - 9 - 10

List your 3 biggest sources of stress:
1.
2.
3.

List any injuries, past or present:

List any medication you are currently taking:

Nutrition

How would you rate your current nutritional regime?

POOR   **AVERAGE**   **PERFECT**

List the top three things you would fix in your nutrition:
1.
2.
3.

How many times do you eat per day?

How much water do you drink?

How many calories do you eat per day *(if known)*?

Do you feel a drop in energy throughout the day?

What supplements are you currently taking *(if any)*?

Exercise

Outside of dance class, what other activities or sports do you take part in?

How often do you train for these sports?
(Check the nature of these sports and their requirements, will they assist or be detrimental to dance performance?)

How many rest days do you have per week?

Rate your current aerobic fitness levels *(endurance):*

    0 - 1 - 2 - 3 - 4 - 5 - 6 - 7 - 8 - 9 - 10

Rate your current level of strength:

    0 - 1 - 2 - 3 - 4 - 5 - 6 - 7 - 8 - 9 - 10

Rate your current level of speed, power and sharpness:

0 - 1 - 2 - 3 - 4 - 5 - 6 - 7 - 8 - 9 - 10

Rate your current level of flexibility / mobility:

0 - 1 - 2 - 3 - 4 - 5 - 6 - 7 - 8 - 9 - 10

Rate your current level of stability, balance & coordination:

0 - 1 - 2 - 3 - 4 - 5 - 6 - 7 - 8 - 9 - 10

Goal Setting

Previous Year:
Looking back over the previous year, how do you rate your performance?

Was there anything you could have done better?

Was there anything that as a coach I could have done better to support your goals?

Forthcoming Year:
What are your main goals for the coming season?

How motivated are you to achieve these goals?

List any obstacle that you feel might stand in the way of you achieving these goals? *(E.g. injury, motivation, holidays.)*

Confidence

How confident are you as a person *(daily life)*?

> 0 - 1 - 2 - 3 - 4 - 5 - 6 - 7 - 8 - 9 - 10

How confident are you in your dance ability?

> 0 - 1 - 2 - 3 - 4 - 5 - 6 - 7 - 8 - 9 - 10

How confident are you on stage?

> 0 - 1 - 2 - 3 - 4 - 5 - 6 - 7 - 8 - 9 - 10

List any factor that may lower your confidence levels:

List any factor that may assist in raising your confidence levels:

Yearly Competition Calendar

In chapter 4 we provided you with sample yearly calendars showing how to best plan your training seasons around your main competitions in that year. Below I have provided you with your own blank yearly calendar. When sitting down with your teacher at the beginning of the season, I want you to fill in your major competitions of the year, then plan your off season, pre-season and in season training phases around these competitions to ensure you are peaking at exactly the right time. Remember that examples can be found in chapter 4.

Month	Competition	Training Phase	Duration
January			
February			
March			
April			
May			
June			
July			
August			
September			
October			
November			
December			

Your Weekly Training Diary

Below is a blank template for you to use to create your own weekly training diary, with your teacher.

Start off by filling in your dance class sessions, then plan your external training and rest days around this. Start by creating a basic training week and increase the volume of sessions slowly, ensuring the intensity does not drop. I have provided you with an example of my own training week below for reference.

A typical week for you may include:

3-4 full dance classes

1 strength session (home or gym based)

1 speed session (interval or sprint based, depending on what phase of training you're in)

2 short core sessions

2 flexibility & mobility sessions

1 full rest day

Training Diary	Morning	Evening
Monday		
Tuesday		
Wednesday		
Thursday		
Friday		
Saturday		
Sunday		

Components to fill in – Dance Class, Strength Training, Speed Training, Core, Flexibility & Mobility, & Rest Days

Example of my training week

Training Diary	Morning	Evening
Monday	Core Session – 20 minutes	Dance Class
Tuesday	Mobility / Flexibility – 20 minutes	Strength Training – 1 hour

Wednesday	Core Session – 20 minutes	Dance Class – 2 hours
Thursday	Mobility / Flexibility – 20 minutes	Sprint Intervals – 1 hour
Friday	-	Dance Class – 2 hours
Saturday	Dance Class or Home Practise	Foam Roll – 20 minutes
Sunday	REST	REST

TRAINING

Aerobic / Anaerobic Fitness Sessions

In part 2 Robert showed you all how to effectively lay out your training schedule for the year. Please find below a yearly training structure along with a breakdown of off season, pre-season and in season training programmes. Remember detailed video demonstrations of all these exercises can be found on the 'Lauren Early' YouTube page to help support your understand and technique

Overview of a yearly training structure for an Irish dancer

Training Goal	Off Season	Pre-Season	In Season	Maintenance
Anaerobic Session	Endurance – up to 3 minutes	Speed endurance / lactic acid zone – 40-60 seconds	Raw speed – 0-15 seconds	Mix between speed endurance & speed

Strength Session	Structural balance / opposing muscle groups	Strength – working on all major strength lifts	Power – focusing on moving the load, fast, sharp and powerful	Mix between strength & power
Dance Class Session: Steps	Learning new steps / breaking down steps	Analysing different sections of the dance, correcting technique & errors	Polishing technique	Mix between pre-season & in season work
Dances	Dancing full dances with minimal recovery (1-2 minutes)	Dancing full dances to failure (3-5 minutes recovery)	3-4 full dances max with ample recovery time to allow heart rate to return to normal. (5-10 minutes)	(Depending on length of time separating competitions. If only a matter of days / a week, strictly in season work only. If 4-8 weeks pre-season, then in season combined.)
Interval based dance work	Endurance Drill work to failure (1-2 minute drills with equal or less recovery)	Lactic acid based drill work to failure (60 second drills with 2 minute recovery)	Speed drills – short & sharp, avoiding failure (15-30 second drills with 2-3 minutes recovery)	Mix between pre-season & in season work

Off Season Training Programme

The goal of an off season phase is to develop a base level of conditioning for the dancer. I have shared below a typical training session plan designed for off season training that will achieve the level of conditioning required. This training session is an interval based session designed to increase and decrease the heart rate intermittently. The focus is not on getting faster each week, but to recover more quickly each week while maintaining the same speed. Please notice that the rest time will be reduced each week to force the body to recover more quickly and still achieve the same speed.

After a thorough warm up, proceed straight into the main session. The full session should last no more than 40 minutes and should be completed 1-2 days per week, scheduled on separate days from your dance class. I recommend completing this session over a 6-8 week period on a soft surface such as a football or soccer field to keep impact at a minimum.

Session 1	Session 2	Session 3
2 minute run @ 75% speed	2 minute run @ 75% speed	2 minute run @ 75% speed
2 minute - slow walk	1 min 50 sec - slow walk	1 min 40 sec - slow walk
Repeat 10 times	Repeat 10 times	Repeat 10 times

Session 4	Session 5	Session 6
2 minutes run @ 75% speed	2 minute run @ 75% speed	2 minute run @ 75% speed
1 min 30 sec - slow walk	1 min 20 sec - slow walk	1 min 10 sec - slow walk
Repeat 10 times	Repeat 10 times	Repeat 10 times

Session 7	Information
2 minutes run 75% speed	Complete a fast 2 minute run at around 85% of your maximum speed. Your rest period will be a slow walk back to your starting position. This rest time will reduce by 10 seconds each week, starting at 2 minutes and ending at 1 minute. Low level fitness dancers can reduce by 5 seconds each week if required
1 minute slow walk	
Repeat 10 times	

Pre-season training programme

The goal of the pre-season training phase is to develop a dancer's speed, strength and lactic acid tolerance. I have shared below a typical training session plan designed for pre-season training that will make the dancer train firmly in the lactic acid zone (40-120 seconds).

In week 1 you will complete 4 x 400m sprints designed to produce full lactic acid at the higher end of the timescale (120 second runs). In week 2 you will complete 8 x 200m sprints to cover the lower end of the timescale (40 second runs) to allow more speed over a shorter distance.

Each session will cover the same total distance (1600m); however, one session will produce higher lactate and the other session will allow for higher speed output. Alternate each session and record your times, with the aim of getting faster every other week.

After a thorough warm up, please go straight into the main session. The full session should last no more than 40-60 minutes and should be completed 1-2 days per week, scheduled on separate days from your dance class. I recommend completing this session over a 6-8 week period on a marked athletics track so that accurate distance can be used.

Session	Breakdown	Rest	Tempo
Session 1	4 x 400m sprints	5-10 minutes	85% speed
Session 2	8 x 200m sprints	2-3 minutes	95% speed
Session 3	4 x 200m sprints	5-10 minutes	85% speed
Session 4	8 x 200m sprints	2-3 minutes	95% speed
Session 5	4 x 400m sprints	5-10 minutes	85% speed
Session 6	8 x 200m sprints	2-3 minutes	95% speed

In Season Sprint Training – Phase 3

The goal of an in season phase is to develop a dancer's acceleration, raw speed, sharpness, explosiveness and reaction times. I have shared below a typical training session plan designed for in season training that will achieve all of these things.

After a thorough warm up, start off by completing the agility drills section. Once completed, move directly onto the sprint training session, as shown below. The full session should last no more than 60 minutes and should be completed 1-2 days per week, scheduled on separate days from your dance class. I recommend completing these sessions over a 6-8 week period on a marked athletics track for the sprint section, so that distance can be measured accurately. I would also suggest using the centre field for the plyometric agility sessions during the warm up, using the softer surface to reduce impact.

In season agility training warm up

Part 1 – Footwork & acceleration

Section	Exercise / Drill	Difficulty Level
1	Fast feet – 2 steps forward / back with 30m forward sprint off	Easy
2	Scissor hops with 30m forward sprint off	Medium
3	Sideways football shuffles with 30m forward sprint off	Hard

Part 2 – Agility & spacial awareness

Section	Exercise / Drill	Difficulty Level
1	Shuttle run	Easy
2	Figure of 8	Medium
3	Z drill	Hard

Part 3 – Plyometrics & Elastic Strength

Section	Exercise / Drill	Difficulty Level
1	Broad jumps / bounds	Easy
2	One-legged scissor hops	Medium
3	Alternating leg bounds (extended running stride)	Hard

Sprint training session

Distance	Distance Divide	Recovery	Goal
Part 1 10 x 30m reaction sprints	No divide – full 30m sprint	Slow walk back	Focus on reaction time with an explosive start. Intermittent & unexpected whistle blows to start. Dancer can also face in the opposite direction, thus creating a sharp rotation followed by a short burst of power.
Part 2 6 x 60m zone sprints	60m divided into 3 x 20m zones Tempo for each zone Fast / Faster / Fastest	1-2 minutes	The zones are made up of 3 x 20m zones, dividing up the full 60m distance. The zones are designed to have the athlete increase their speed as they enter each zone.
Part 3 6 x 120m zone sprints	120m divided into 3 x 40m zones Tempo for each zone Fast / Faster / Fastest	2-3 minutes	The zones are made up of 3 x 40m zones, dividing up the full 60m distance. The zones are designed to have the athlete increase their speed as they enter each zone.

TRAINING

Strength & Structural Balance Sessions

Throughout the book we explained that all muscles work in pairs and discussed the problem of overusing certain muscle groups, which creates imbalances within the dancer. Below is a table listing the major muscle groups used by a dancer and listed opposite is the opposing muscle group that is generally underused.

This table is an example of the most common imbalance found in a dancer; a proper assessment would need to be conducted individually to determine your exact weaknesses. I have also recommended one exercise that will help to strengthen the opposing muscle groups to help regain full structural balance.

The table lists the groups starting at the shoulders and working down to the feet.

Major muscle (overused)	Opposing muscle (underused)	Exercise to fix imbalance
Shoulders (deltoids)	Upper back (latissimus dorsi)	Pull ups or lateral pull downs
Chest (pectorals)	Upper mid back (rhomboids)	Seated row / shoulder retractions
Stomach (abs)	Lower back (erector spinae)	Hyperextensions / lower back raises
Hip – raising leg up and down (iliopsoas)	Bum (gluteus maximus)	Full range squats / split squats
Hip – moving leg out to side and in (hip adductor)	Bum (gluteus medius)	Side step ups / lateral resistance band walking
Thigh – (quadriceps)	Thigh (hamstrings)	Lying hamstring curl
Lower leg – calf (gastrocnemius)	Lower leg – shin (tibialis anterior)	Toe raises

The programme below shows how all the above exercises can be programmed into a full training session. I recommend this training session be completed in the off season training phase for 6-8 weeks, where structural balance is a priority. I also recommend including it throughout the year when your strength or ability improves. This session incorporates the full body and should take no longer than 45-60 minutes, including a thorough warm up.

Exercise No.	Exercise Name	Sets	Reps	Rest
WARM UP				
Exercise 1 Upper back	Pull ups or lateral pull downs	4	8–10	90 seconds
Exercise 2 Mid back	Seated row / resistance band row	4	10–12	60 seconds
Exercise 3 Lower back	Hyperextensions / lower back raises	3	12–15	45 seconds
REST 3 MINUTES				
Exercise 4 Legs	Dumbbell squats	4	8–10	90 seconds
Exercise 5 Legs	Split squats on platform	4	10–12	60 seconds
Exercise 5 Legs	Side step ups on platform	3	12–15	45 seconds
REST 3 MINUTES				
Exercise 6 Hamstrings	Hamstring curl – machine or stability ball	4	10–12	45 seconds
Exercise 7 Tibialis anterior (shin)	Toe raises on platform	4	15–20	45 seconds

This programme is a full body workout. Each exercise is listed along with an alternative exercise for beginners or home-based training. The amount of sets is how many times you will repeat the entire exercise. The amount of reps is how many times you will complete the exercise within any given set.

For example, if we look at this scenario: 4 x 10-12 reps with 90 seconds recovery. This would mean there are 4 sets and the exercise is completed 10-12 times within each set. The rest after each set is 90 seconds, then the next set begins.

NUTRITION

7 Day Nutrition Programme

Below is a sample nutrition programme; it's one that I closely followed throughout my competitive dance career. The nutrition plan consists of a high carbohydrate, high protein, low fat diet designed to optimise maximum performance and recovery.

Monday to Friday are standard calorie days made up of high carbohydrate, high protein and low healthy fats.

Saturday is a higher calorie and carbohydrate loading day to boost recovery, metabolism and performance.

Sunday is a rest day, therefore treated as a low carbohydrate day.

Below are my statistics, to which the plan was created:

Basal Metabolic Rate (BMR) = 1500 calories

Target Daily Energy Expenditure = 2168 calories

Nutritional Goal – To Fuel Performance

Note: Please use your own statistics and goals calculated in chapter 7 to establish your own nutritional requirements and alter accordingly.

High Protein – High Carb – Low Fat Athlete Performance Plan Day 1 – Monday	
Meal 1 – BREAKFAST	**Meal 4 – DINNER**
Before food, drink squeezed lemon in lukewarm water & take supplements *(see list)* Smoked salmon – 100g Spinach – 100g Cashew nuts – 25g	Beef steak – 150g Half avocado & sweet potato – 200g Green vegetables – 100g
Meal 2 – MORNING SNACK	**MEAL 5 – BEFORE BED**
Fat-free Greek yogurt – 170g Whey protein – 10g Peanut butter – 10g Oats – 40g *(mix to create dessert)*	Oats – 40g Dark chocolate 85% – 4 squares Blueberries – 50g Whey protein – 30g *(mix to create a dessert)*
Meal 3 – LUNCH	**WORKOUT**
Cod fillet – 150g Half avocado & basmati rice – 60g Green vegetables – 100g	Before & during: electrolyte sports drink After: whey protein – 40g Pineapple – 200g

High Protein – High Carb – Low Fat Athlete Performance Plan Day 2 – Tuesday	
Meal 1 – BREAKFAST	**Meal 4 – DINNER**
Before food, drink squeezed lemon in lukewarm water & take supplements *(see list)* 3 free range eggs & 2 rashers bacon Spinach – 100g Brazil nuts – 25g	Extra lean mince burgers – 150g Half avocado & jasmine rice – 60g Green vegetables – 100g
Meal 2 – MORNING SNACK	**MEAL 5 – BEFORE BED**
Fat-free Greek yogurt – 170g Whey protein – 10g Peanut butter – 10g Oats – 40g *(mix to create dessert)*	Oats – 40g Flaxseeds – 10g Blueberries – 50g Whey protein – 30g *(mix to create a dessert)*
Meal 3 – LUNCH	**WORKOUT**
Turkey – 150g Half avocado & sweet potato – 200g Green vegetables – 100g	Before & during: electrolyte sports drink After: whey protein – 40g Figs – 100g

High Protein – High Carb – Low Fat Athlete Performance Plan Day 3 – Wednesday	
Meal 1 – BREAKFAST	**Meal 4 – DINNER**
Before food, drink squeezed lemon in lukewarm water & take supplements *(see list)* Steak – 150g Kale – 100g Macadamia nuts – 25g	Salmon fillet – 150g Half avocado & basmati rice – 60g Green vegetables – 100g

Meal 2 – MORNING SNACK	MEAL 5 – BEFORE BED
Fat-free Greek yogurt – 170g Whey protein – 10g Peanut butter – 10g Oats – 40g *(mix to create dessert)*	Oats – 40g Dark chocolate 85% – 4 squares Blueberries – 50g Whey protein – 30g *(mix to create a dessert)*
Meal 3 – LUNCH	WORKOUT
Chicken breast – 150g Half avocado & boiled baby potatoes – 200g Green vegetables – 100g	Before & during: electrolyte sports drink After: whey protein – 40g Bananas – 100g

High Protein – High Carb – Low Fat Athlete Performance Plan Day 4 – Thursday	
Meal 1 – BREAKFAST	Meal 4 – DINNER
Before food, drink squeezed lemon in lukewarm water & take supplements *(see list)* Smoked salmon & scrambled egg – 150g Spinach – 100g Macadamia nuts – 25g	Turkey mince chilli – 150g Basmati rice – 60g Green vegetables – 100g
Meal 2 – MORNING SNACK	MEAL 5 – BEFORE BED
Fat-free Greek yogurt – 170g Whey protein – 10g Peanut Butter – 10g Oats – 40g *(mix to create dessert)*	Oats – 40g Flaxseeds – 10g Blueberries – 50g Whey protein – 30g *(mix to create a dessert)*
Meal 3 – LUNCH	WORKOUT
Cod fillet – 150g Half avocado & boiled baby potatoes – 200g Green vegetables – 100g	Before & during: electrolyte sports drink After: whey protein – 40g Pineapple – 200g

High Protein – High Carb – Low Fat Athlete Performance Plan Day 5 – Friday	
Meal 1 – BREAKFAST	**Meal 4 – DINNER**
Before food, drink squeezed lemon in lukewarm water & take supplements *(see list)* 3 free range egg omelette Spinach – 100g Brazil nuts – 25g	Beef strip stir-fry - 150g Jasmine rice – 60g Green vegetables – 100g
Meal 2 – MORNING SNACK	**MEAL 5 – BEFORE BED**
Fat-free Greek yogurt – 170g Whey protein – 10g Peanut Butter – 10g Oats – 40g *(mix to create dessert)*	Oats – 40g Dark chocolate 85% – 4 squares Blueberries – 50g Whey protein – 30g *(mix to create a dessert)*
Meal 3 – LUNCH	**WORKOUT**
Turkey breast – 150g Half avocado & sweet potatoes – 200g Green vegetables – 100g	Before & during: electrolyte sports drink After: whey protein – 40g Dried apricots – 200g

High Protein – High Carb – Low Fat Athlete Performance Plan Day 6 – Saturday	
Meal 1 – BREAKFAST	**Meal 4 – DINNER**
Before food, drink squeezed lemon in lukewarm water & take supplements *(see list)* Muesli - Granola - 60g Protein Shake - 30g	**Cheat High Carb Meal**

Meal 2 – MORNING SNACK	MEAL 5 – BEFORE BED
Fat-free Greek yogurt – 170g Whey protein – 10g Peanut Butter – 10g Oats – 60g *(mix to create dessert)*	Oats – 40g Flaxseeds – 10g Blueberries – 50g Whey protein – 30g *(mix to create a dessert)*
Meal 3 – LUNCH	**WORKOUT**
Rice cakes – 8 cakes Topped with banana – 100g Honey – 2 teaspoons	Before & during: electrolyte sports drink After: whey protein – 40g Kiwi – 200g

LOW CARB DAY Athlete Performance Plan Day 7 – Sunday	
Meal 1 – BREAKFAST	**Meal 4 – DINNER**
Before food, drink squeezed lemon in lukewarm water & take supplements *(see list)* Steak – 150g Kale – 100g Almonds – 40g	Salmon fillet – 150g Half avocado Green vegetables – 100g
Meal 2 – MORNING SNACK	**MEAL 5 – BEFORE BED**
Fat-free Greek yogurt – 170g Whey protein – 10g Peanut butter – 20g *(mix to create dessert)*	Flaxseeds – 10g Blueberries – 50g Whey protein – 30g Dark chocolate 85%– 6 squares *(mix to create a dessert)*
Meal 3 – LUNCH	**WORKOUT**
Chicken breast – 150g Half avocado Green vegetables – 100g	REST DAY

Acknowledgements

I would like to thank Robert McAvoy for the knowledge he kindly shared throughout this book. We are truly blessed to have a strength coach of his stature who has dedicated so much time and interest into the ongoing development of our sport.

I would also like to thank my dancing teachers, Seaneen and Gavin Doherty; without you my achievements in this sport would not have been possible.

I dedicate this book to my family and grandparents, John and Peggy Smith, Molly Early, and the late Harry Early, who never got to see me win a world title, although I always knew he was looking down on me. Thank you for the shoulders to cry on, for the support through my highs and lows, for lifting my spirits up when things didn't go my way, for the laughter and wild celebrations we shared together, but most of all for believing in me!!

Finally, I would like to thank the readers of this book. Your passion and drive to succeed and learn has made this book possible and I cannot wait to share your journey to the top with each of you.

As Irish dancers we truly are part of one big family.

Thank you all,

Lauren x

Bibliography

[1] Rowbottom, David J. (2000). 'Periodization of Training.' In Garrett, William E.; Kirkendall, Donald T. Periodization of Training. Philadelphia: Lippincott Williams & Wilkins. p. 499. ISBN 9780683034219 Retrieved April 5 2015.

[2] Arnd Kruger (1973). 'Periodization or Peaking at the right time', in: Track Technique 54 (1973), pp.1720- 1724.

[3] Wikipedia The Free Encyclopedia. Sports Periodization. 2009 [online] Available from page 1 on
http://en.wikipedia.org/wiki/Sports_periodization#cite_note-Rowbottom-1 [accessed April 5 2015].

[4] Drechsler, A. (1998) 'The Weightlifting Encyclopedia: A Guide To World Class Performance.' A Is A Communications.

[5] Hale, J. (2006) Strength training for children. *Brian Mackenzie's Successful Coaching,* (ISSN 1745-7513/ 35/ September), p. 3-4.

[6] Siff, M. (2000) 'Facts and Fallacies of Fitness'. Mel Siff.

[7] Australian Sport – Weight Training for Preadolescents – http://www.ausport.gov.au/__data/assets/pdf_file/0009/145971/Article_weight_training_preadolescent_strength_training_Narelle_Sibte.pdf [accessed April 8 2015].

[8] DiFiori, J (2002) 'Overuse injuries in young athletes: An overview.' Athletic Therapy Today; 7(6): 25-29.

[9] Ramsey, J. Blimkie, C. Smith, K. Garner, S. Macdougall, D & Sale, D. (1990) Strength training effects in prepubescent boys. Med Sci in Spt & Ex, 22(5): 605-614.

[10] Faigenbaum, A (2002) 'Resistance training for adolescent athletes.' Athletic Therapy Today, 7(6): 30-35.

[11] 8. Payne, V. Morrow, J. Johnson, L & Dalton, S (1997) 'Resistance training in children and youth: a meta analysis.' Research Quarterly for Exercise and Sport, 60:80-88.

[12] Poliquin, Charles. 'Strength Sensei'S Blog : Balance Training – Yes Or No?'. Official Website for Charles R Poliquin: Strength Training, Nutrition, Articles, Books, Motivation, Supplementation. N.p., 2014. Web. 9 Apr. 2015.

[13] Poliquin, Charles (1997). *The Poliquin Principles*. CA: Dayton Writers Group. 17.

[14] JC, Gergley. 'Acute Effect Of Passive Static Stretching On Lower-Body Strength In Moderately Trained Men.' – Pubmed - NCBI'. Ncbi.nlm.nih.gov. N.p., 2015. Web. 22 May 2015.

[15] Simic L, et al. 'Does Pre-Exercise Static Stretching Inhibit Maximal Muscular Performance? A Meta-Analytical Review.' – Pubmed – NCBI. Ncbi.nlm.nih.gov. N.p., 2015. Web. 22 May 2015.

[16] Critchell, M. (2002) 'Warm ups for soccer: a dynamic approach', Spring City, PA: Reedswain, p. 5.

[17] Nhlbi.nih.gov. 'What Is Cholesterol? – NHLBI, NIH'. N.p., 2015. Web. 11 May 2015.

[18] Kresser, Chris. 'The Diet-Heart Myth: Cholesterol And Saturated Fat Are Not The Enemy.' *Chris Kresser*. N.p., 2013. Web. 11 May 2015.

[19] Mensink rp, et al. 'Effects of dietary fatty acids and carbohydrates on the ratio of serum total to hdl cholesterol and on serum lipids and apolipoproteins: A meta-ana... – pubmed – ncbi'. ncbi.nlm.nih.gov. n.p.,

2015. web. 11 may 2015.

[20] Guyenet, Stephan. 'Whole Health Source: Does Dietary Saturated Fat Increase Blood Cholesterol? An Informal Review Of Observational Studies'. *Wholehealthsource.blogspot.co.uk*. N.p., 2011. Web. 11 May 2015.

[21] Siri-Tarino PW, et al. 'Meta-Analysis Of Prospective Cohort Studies Evaluating The Association Of Saturated Fat With Cardiovascular Disease. – Pubmed – NCBI'. *Ncbi.nlm.nih.gov*. N.p., 2015. Web. 11 May 2015.

[22] Yamagishi K, et al. 'Dietary Intake Of Saturated Fatty Acids And Mortality From Cardiovascular Disease In Japanese: The Japan Collaborative Cohort Study For Evaluation ... – Pubmed – NCBI'. *Ncbi.nlm.nih.gov*. N.p., 2015. Web. 11 May 2015.

[23] U.S. Department of Agriculture and U.S. Department of Health and Human Services. 'Dietary Guidelines for Americans, 2010.' 7th Edition, Washington, DC: U.S. Government Printing Office, December 2010.